40

THE PICADOR BOOK OF

40

40 WRITERS INSPIRED BY
A NUMBER

Edited by Charlotte Greig

PICADOR

First published 2012 by Picador
an imprint of Pan Macmillan Ltd, a division of Macmillan Publishers Limited
Pan Macmillan, 20 New Wharf Road, London N1 9RR
Basingstoke and Oxford
Associated companies throughout the world
www.panmacmillan.com

ISBN 978-1-4472-1904-0

1 3 5 7 9 8 6 4 2

A CIP catalogue record for this book is available from
the British Library.

Printed and bound by CPI Group (UK) Ltd, Croydon, CR0 4YY

Visit **www.picador.com** to read more about all our books
and to buy them. You will also find features, author interviews and
news of any author events, and you can sign up for e-newsletters
so that you're always first to hear about our new releases.

Introduction

On 6 October 1972, Picador published its first list of eight paperbacks, a list that immediately highlighted Picador's ambition and cultural breadth. The titles included great writing from Latin America (Jorge Luis Borges's *A Personal Anthology*), Europe (Hermann Hesse's *Rosshalde*), America (Richard Brautigan's *Trout Fishing in America*), and Britain (Angela Carter's *Heroes and Villains*), and within a few years, Picador had established itself as the pre-eminent publisher of contemporary fiction and non-fiction.

Forty years on, Picador still strives to publish the finest fiction and non-fiction. We now publish in all formats, hardback, paperback and digital, and have a prize-winning poetry list, under the guidance of editor Don Paterson, that has established itself as the finest list of contemporary poets around.

To celebrate our 40th Anniversary, we asked thirty-nine writers and one artist to produce a piece of work loosely connected to the number 40. From Matteo Pericoli's infinity symbol (in forty lines) that graces the cover, to the thirty-nine Picador writers who have interpreted the theme in so many original ways, we have a wonderful selection of stories, poems, diatribes and meditations. I hope that you will enjoy pieces by established favourites as well as discovering new stars and that you will agree with us that life for Picador certainly continues very healthily at 40.

Paul Baggaley
Picador Publisher

CONTENTS

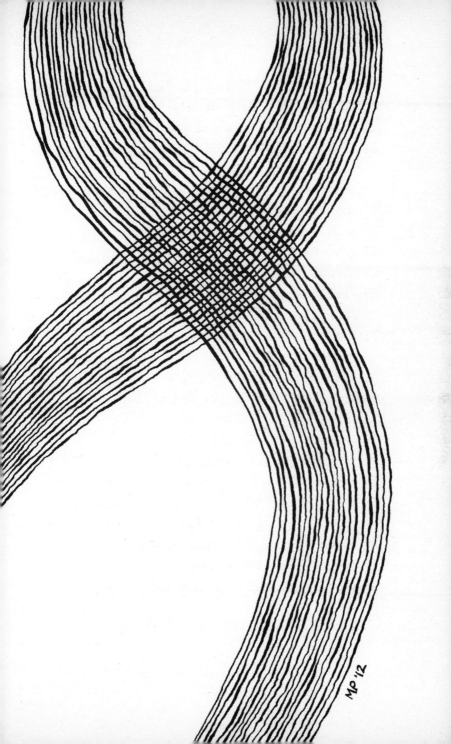

MEGAN ABBOTT

Forty Cakes

You would, very likely, be surprised to know there are hundreds and maybe thousands of Americans of a certain age who hear the word "forty" and, from somewhere in the warps and winnows of their brain, comes the echo of a peculiar phrase, "Forty cakes."

Forty cakes. In this short, quizzical locution, there lies something both utterly au courant and deeply eternal about the power of books.

Let me explain: Several months ago, I came upon a particular fascinating example of an Internet meme—one of those insidiously contagious concepts, conceits, catchphrases (e.g., "snakes on a plane," "rick rolling," which involves sending putatively serious emails that link recipients to rollicking Rick Astley clips from the 1980s) that spread across the web, social networks, even among real live people at cocktail parties.

These memes, transitory but powerful, seem on the surface to be nothing more than in-jokes, serving as a means of distinguishing those in the know (and those who knew *first*—before, as another old meme goes, it "jumped the shark") from the vast unhip. Yet one could easily argue that, rather than a means of excluding, memes are, in an increasingly sprawling and faceless world, a means of *connecting*.

Consider the case of the forty cakes. Its derivation lies in a 1978 publication called *The Super Dictionary*, a children's book that used Batman, Wonder Woman, Flash and other superheroes from the DC Comics universe to teach young readers their numbers and the meanings of basic words. Here is how it educated readers on the number forty:

> When no one was looking, Lex Luthor
> took forty cakes. He took 40 cakes.
> That's as many as four tens.
> And that's terrible.

The associated illustration shows the famed nemesis of Superman in full sprint, yanking a rolling cart of desserts behind him. It's mystifying on many levels—why would a monomaniacal super-villain bother with stealing pastries? What does he intend to do with them? And, perhaps most puzzlingly, what are we to make of the fact that the desserts in question are clearly pies?

And so, in various forms, portions of the text, its illustration, are scattered across not only the Internet but, in a canny bit of meta-meming, back into comic books themselves (fans rejoiced at a reference to it in a recent issue of *Superman*). The most tenacious portion of the meme seems to be the last line—*And that's terrible*—which has become an "in-group" shorthand for an extraneous assertion.

Beyond its puzzling content, one of the fascinations of Forty Cakes is the way the text "scans," its odd meter, the repetition and its unusual phrasing, calling to mind an attenuated haiku, even a zen kōan. Its idiosyncratic rhythm lingers in the head, like a phrase of a childhood song, like a line from a fairy tale ("Grandmother, what a great mouth you have!"). And, of course, when we riff on it, we are whispering in the ears of all of us who know the hidden reference. An in-joke with authentic emotional heft. We are children again, sharing secrets behind our hands.

Forty Cakes, then, is not a meme that sprang from the Internet; it was merely expressed there. It derives from something older, more primal but also more internal and personal. It derives from our childhoods. Not the "generational" childhood of common pop-cultural references, but the part of childhood we all share. Our half-forgotten memory of what it feels like to be at the age when we are trying to figure out the world, piece by piece. When everything is mysterious and we yearn to unravel the mysteries of life. A yearning that, as the years skitter by and experience feels more like a burden than a beacon, we conveniently forget.

Ironically, I don't explicitly recall *The Super Dictionary* and don't quite trust the faint déjà vu I felt when I first came upon the Forty Cakes meme. Still, it hums in me because of the kindred memories it stirs. We all remember moments from our youth when knowledge was passed to us that seemed strange, mystical. That didn't seem to fit. As a child, I was a rapacious reader of *Archie* comic books, which documented the sunny lives of fictional small-town teenagers. My favorite issues were always those devoted to Betty and Veronica, the main heroines of the series, both of whom fought for the favor of boy-next-door Archie and who comprised the archetypal good girl-bad girl dyad that I've come to realize has—in its light (teen movies) and dark (films noir) forms—informed the books I love to read and the ones I write.

Decades later, the plots or intrigues of virtually all of the Betty and Veronica tales have tucked themselves into various inaccessible corners of my head. But one has always remained palpable. In my memory, Betty, the fair-haired girl-next-door, develops wildly crimson blotches on her cheeks. I recalled with stunning vividness the image of Betty standing before a mirror staring at her face, the cheek blotches recalling bloody smears. Over the years, I have doubted the memory. How could this have been a real *Archie* comic plotline? *Archie*, the world of first kisses, school dances and soda-shop hijinks.

In recent weeks, however, inspired by the "Forty Cakes" meme, I have tracked down the comic in question. It belongs to a multi-issue *Archie* storyline called "Betty Cooper, Betty Cooper"—an attempt to mimic the 1970s American TV show *Mary Hartman, Mary Hartman*, a soap opera parody. To my mind, however, "Betty Cooper" owes far more to *Dark Shadows*, the gothic vampire TV series I loved as a girl. Rife with plot strands about bloodlines, witches, gypsies, secret fortunes, "Betty Cooper" is narrated in the breathless, hushed tones of a sensation novel.

Paging through the comic a few weeks ago, I was elated to note that there is indeed a plot line in which Betty discovers, as I had recalled, inexplicable red blotches on her face, as does Veronica, suggesting the two might be sisters. Suddenly, I remembered my initial shock over this—what would it mean if the already complicated Betty and Veronica relationship (sometimes they are friends, sometimes arch-enemies, sometimes ego and id) developed this additional complication? It was almost more than my seven-year-old brain could bear. I recalled pondering it endlessly. Could a girl be good *and* bad?

The experience of returning to the comic highlighted to me just what we see in the "Forty Cakes" meme: the capacity of books we discover as children—particularly the ones that stir and puzzle us—to burrow into our heads, to inform, in ways large and small, the way we see the world but also understand ourselves, our own fascinations. As one online *Archie* aficionado recalled fondly, "That 'Betty Cooper, Betty Cooper' story was where I first learned the meaning of the word 'bloodcurdling.' The dark world that might lie underneath the pleasant small-town of the *Archie* comics clearly enthralled me, stuck with me in ways hundreds of other comics did not. Perhaps indeed led me to other similar tales of "the underneath," from *Peyton Place* to *Twin Peaks*.

There is another layer to this, of course. And it resounds as I think of Picador's extraordinary forty years, forty years of books that have made deep impressions, both visible and invisible, on millions of readers. Indeed, while comic books have a unique capacity to stamp our brains, traditional books hold still more magic because of the pictures we conjure in our own heads. How many of us recall our first introduction to, say, Jane Eyre's red room or Fitzgerald's glittering East Egg? When we first found ourselves "painting" physical spaces, whole worlds in our imagination? Making them real and their mysteries vivid as those in our own lives?

Then, the Forty Cakes meme is not merely the dross of a buzzy, irony-laden culture of engineered advertisements, viral marketing or cynical hoaxes and pranks. It speaks to the power of books we read as children, our minds still open, unblinking, rapt. And they linger in the brain, their rhythms pulsing through us decades later, whittling their way into our unconscious, to unsettle and unearth our most hidden corners. And just as potent as the knowledge we gained from books (from learning the number forty to learning about the French Revolution), is the knowledge that seemed to elude us, or be just beyond our grasp. Part of the fundamental power of books—their true exceptionalism—is the way they can, if weird and wonderful enough, both illuminate and obfuscate. Not just as children, but always.

Books write (or, later, rewrite) the world for us, especially the hidden worlds lurking behind the worlds we know so well. All books are ghost stories in that way, pulling back heavy curtains and showing us things we both never knew and things we somehow knew all along, on some lower register. The cadences of long forgotten sentences that sneakily tattooed themselves on our brains . . . they last. And that's beautiful.

SHALOM AUSLANDER

Three Under Three

Much has been said about this year's Three Under Three contest, much of it false, much of it accusatory and much of it of a vitriolic personal nature directed at myself. I would like to address some of these issues head-on, and in as straightforward and honest a manner as I can.

In the first place, it is true that I turned forty this year, and it is equally true that, for the fortieth time, my writing did not make it into the *New Yorker* "Forty Under Forty" issue, or *Granta*'s "Forty Under Forty" issue, or the *LA Times*' "Forty Faces Under Forty" issue or the *Guardian*'s annual "Forty American Writers Under Forty to Watch" or even McSweeney's "Forty Writers Under Forty Who Live Near Us in Brooklyn and We Hang Out With Quite a Bit or At Least Would Like To." There are many reasons for that, not the least of which is that they are all shitty magazines dedicated to the death of writing and literature. Would I like to have been included? Of course. We all want external validation of our years of sweat and toil. But to suggest my exclusion from these lists in the last year of my eligibility for them somehow affected my judging of the Paradigm Day School "Three Under Three" Writing Contest is not just baseless slander, it is armchair psychology of the very worst kind.

To remind everyone: I was asked (without any offer of remuneration at all, mind you) to read through the many submissions and choose "the three writers under three years of age who capture the inventiveness and vitality of contemporary American pre-school literature."

I shall come back to this.

Much of the vitriol directed at me has come from the family and friends of young Zachary Goldfarb, and so I would like to address his submission first. I can understand their disappointment, but frankly, Zachary's "story" was nothing of the kind. Here is his submission, copied without alteration:

"David likes the snow.

The snow is cold.

So is ice."

Well, whoop-de-fucking-doo. "David" (we can assume this is a fictional Zuckerman-like stand-in for Zachary himself) likes the snow. Do I need Mr. Goldfarb to tell me this? Of what consequence can this preference for snow be? Where, more importantly, is the story? David simply is. He does nothing, desires nothing. He exists, if that, and nothing more. If perhaps we had been told that David did not like the snow, and the snow was cold, we could at least imagine the beginnings of a story, a conflict, a drama: perhaps David will try to find warmth (a quest of sorts)? Perhaps he will come, in the end, to like the snow? But as it is written, all we know is that David likes the snow. If there is a connection between David's appreciation of snow and the relative coldness of the snow and ice, it is left to the reader to discern. Should I reward this? The snow is cold, Zachary, that is true. So is the ice. And so is the world, and so is life. Get used to it.

The second submission, from Sally Ryan, two:

"Michael is nice. He shares his toys and never hits. Today he was sick. I hope he feels better."

Good God. Where to begin? Let's grant, for just a moment, that when Ms. Ryan penned this little tale, she knew that in future chapters the obviously Jesus-like simplistic character of Michael would deepen and somehow become more complex and multi-dimensional. And let's also grant that the plot issue she sets up here (Michael's illness and her concomitant hope for his recuperation) will be resolved in the pages to come. Let's grant all that. But shall we also grant that this is fiction, which the contest expressly limits itself to? Shall we just ignore the fact that there is in fact a Michael in Ms. Ryan's class, a Michael who is known the school over for sharing his toys and never hitting and had, at the time of the writing of this "story," a very nasty flu? What lesson would we be teaching Sally if we let her win a fiction contest with a clearly non-fictional work? What we have here in Sally Ryan is our very own James Frey, but rather than faking reality, she has chosen to fake fiction. I, for one, am sickened.

And so we come to the winner:

"Harley was our dog. She is dead now. I want to get a cat."

At last. This is art. This is pathos. This is story. And yes, this is also my own entry. But can you not see the difference between this small gem and the earlier (failed) attempts of Mr. Goldfarb and Ms. Ryan? Here we have sadness and rage and pain and even, yes, in the very last sentence, a flicker of hope for the future. A beginning: Harley *was* our dog. A middle: She *is* dead now. An ending, a ray of light: I want *to get* a cat. A simple story, but a deceptive one, for the main character has changed, has he not? He is hardened now, slightly older and more knowing of the vicissitudes of life. He loved a dog, and yet still, he wants a cat. He can't go on, he goes on. Is that not the modern Everyman? Falling, in our humanity, in love; witnessing, in our mortality, death; and rising, thanks to our damned humanity, to love once more. I read this story and hope, despite myself, for the future of literature. I looked, as I had been instructed, for "the three writers under three years of age who capture the inventiveness and vitality of contemporary American pre-school literature," and I found not three. I found not even one. And so I submitted my own. If that annoys some of the other entrants, or their parents, perhaps they should think of literature before themselves.

Thank you.

(The award ceremony will be held at Skytop Bar and Lounge, Saturday night, 9 PM)

JOHN BANVILLE

Life Ends at Forty

I knew it was coming, of course I did; how would I not? After all, the end of being thirty-nine is being forty. Yet that particular birthday arrived with the force of a blow to the solar plexus, and knocked the wind out of me. Somehow nothing was to be the same, afterwards, I cannot say in what way, exactly, only I know everything was changed. I think of a summer day in the palmy South climbing towards noon, then resting for an hour or two, panting gently in the lemon sunlight and the tawny dust of the piazza, then starting on the long decline towards shadows, and dusk, and night. Things as they were in the morning are different in the afternoon; the same things, but in an altered light. After I became forty, my life took umbrage.

Granted, there is another possible end to being thirty-nine. When we are young—and nowadays youth lasts very much longer than it did heretofore—death is a preposterous scandal. There is the evidence of it happening to others, all the time, all over the place, sometimes even to the young; but that does not mean that it will happen to *us*. Youth conceives of itself as impervious, indestructible, unslayable. We know we shall have to go, sooner or later—much, much later—but that fact is as hazily unlikely as, say, the dimensions of the universe, or the existence of rainbows. Larkin got it right, as usual:

> *It stands plain as a wardrobe, what we know,*
> *Have always known, know that we can't escape,*
> *Yet can't accept.*

So there I was, in the prime of life, hardly more than a stripling in my own eyes, but time had its own foul plan for me. There was a birthday party. I remember doing nothing but sit in an armchair with my back to a big picture window, greeting party guests with a wan and sickly smile, like a patient receiving visitors in a particularly homely hospital. Someone brought me a bowl of cherries—an actual, hand-blown bowl, filled with real cherries—and I looked at it and thought, *Yes, that's what it all amounts to, a miserable bloody bowl of cherries!*

No milestone—millstone?—birthday since has been as hard to greet as that one. The fulcrum of my life tipped to the left that day, and it has been dipping ever since. Now that I am in the springtime of my senescence—as Gore Vidal wonderfully said of Ronald Reagan—I regard the future with the same scepticism that my pre-forty self used to hold up as a shield against the prospect of death. There is a certain thin comedy to be derived from the spectacle of the gradual dissolution of the self. Yes, the great discovery I have made is that mortal decay is funny. Which is not to say that I shall be laughing all the way to my deathbed; not a laugh, not even a smile, but a rictus, and perhaps a hollow chuckle. When the day comes it will be, as Beckett observes, a day like any other, only shorter. Until then, let us have as much of cakes and ale as we can consume.

Oh, and next month I shall be eligible for the old-age pension.

ROBIN BLACK

Cinderella

On her fortieth birthday, she wakes up thinking of the great tower clock.

They had been outside, dancing. They had twirled a path away from the grand ballroom, away from the staring eyes of the glittering crowd, his arm around her waist, his hand on the small of her back. And they were in motion, motion, motion . . . and then, in the spin of it, even as she shivered from the chilly night air, from his touch, from the brush of his jaw against her forehead, she had noticed the clock at the top of the tower, lighted, soaring, inviting as little argument as her step-mother's voice. 11:40.

Only twenty minutes to go, she had thought. *Don't forget to pay attention. Whatever you do, don't lose track of the time.*

That was twenty-three years ago.

And of course she did lose track of time.

At forty past the hour, she knows, the mind shifts to what is left. Forty past becomes twenty to. If you are in a hurry, it is the minute at which you begin to believe that you may make it to the anticipated hour after all. Twenty minutes is not so long to wait. But if you are savoring something, if you are wanting to hold what you have, it is the minute at which grief steals in. Forty past. Twenty to.

She had known that night that the time was flying by. She had seen the hour looming, but had set her understanding aside. Not for the pleasure of being with him – though it was a pleasure, indeed – but because at twenty to the hour, forty past, she began to dread what lay ahead for her. What was this time she had been given, after all? Not the first evening of an easy, coddled life. Not as she had been told up to that point. But the only night she would ever have away from misery. This hour, the last in which she could feel delight, could feel at all, so numb had she become in her own home, among her family, among her cinders, tending her fires.

Just beyond the foot of her bed now are the forty roses the Prince has sent, arranged not in a bunch, but in a line. A clock of sorts, though not the helpful kind. The kind that only tells you what has gone, not what remains.

It doesn't matter that it all turned out as it did, a better life than she had believed she would have, because what good came of that night came only by luck. Or by the design of some unseen, uncontrollable powers in the ether. The fairies. The dead. It wasn't because of anything she herself did. It wasn't because she had looked up at that clock, and seeing how little time there was left, had held on to each second, savoring it, had forced awareness into herself, had banished her carelessness for the ticking, the loss, the march. Had hoarded the moments. She had been too afraid of the dwindling count so had spun and spun and spun and spun, until she forgot what she knew. It chills her now to think that had he never come for her, had she never left that home of pain and ash, she would have been left only with a memory that was nothing but a twirling blur. And with Time for her closest company, mocking her for how she had once squandered it for fear of having it pass.

She rises from her bed and walks toward the roses, and then beyond, to the window from which she can see for miles, the hills and valleys, the forests and, far in the distance, the snowy mountains too. The little homes in which so many people live. The rare grand castles that rival her own, tiny toys from this vantage point. She feels the cool air just outside, and she thinks about the dank darkness of the chimneys she once stared up into as though she might be able to fly through them into another life. About the cooling cinders. About the crumbling ash. And she thinks again about the tower clock rising high behind her, destined never to lose an argument, forever a part of the structure in which she stands.

DAVE BOLING

Miry Clay

Carter types: "When the rainy season settles upon the city, the library swells with homeless smelling of wet wool and fortified wine." Good rhythm, he thinks, evocative. And the wool-and-wine phrasing flows better than the off-putting mushrooms-and-mold image he used in the first draft. He sniffs the air for other descriptive options.

Before his newspaper went bankrupt, he edited the words of others for thirty years, and he finds he's every bit as critical of his own writing as he was of others. Even this newly revised lead sentence feels condescending. Probably unfairly presumptive, too. Some of them sharing the library with him this day may have addictions other than alcohol, or have been cut adrift by afflictions outside their control. Carter hits the "End" key and "Backspace," enjoying the deconstructive power of gobbling letters: eniw deifitorf dna.

And upon further thought: Are they homeless, necessarily? He highlights the word "homeless" and replaces it with "unfortunates." Certainly they are that. He has seen a man wash his socks in the men's room. He strangled the saturated fabric over the sink and then pulled the socks over the hand-drier blowholes, inflating them like limp-gray dirigibles.

He returns to the home keys and tries again. "They sit in mute clusters, passing suspicious glances at the group of students and writers who share the quiet corner of the library on this upper level." Wait, better to just mention the glances and allow the reader to infer a suspicion. He highlights the entire paragraph and again taps the "Delete" key on his laptop, which is now so worn at its concave belly that only "D . . . e" remain visible.

Carter scans the scene over the top of his reading glasses and taps: "Modern institutional furniture . . . at angles in small groups . . . northwestern nomads taking shelter in this hermitage of books." Or "haven" of books? Or "sanctuary of literature?" He deletes the mention of books entirely; they do not seem interested in the literature. This is a dry place to nap and wash socks, he thinks, wondering if there was not a place better suited to their needs.

"Cuts hit shelters . . . nothing we can do," Security Bill told Carter one time, his phrases always sounding as if broadcast over a police-scanner. "Long as they stay awake and read something . . . " Security Bill navigates the floors of the library with the stride of a beat cop, tapping the nodders on the shoulder as polite enforcement.

Carter notes the behavior of the group, drifting off in shifts, rotating "sentry" duty so that one would cough or clear a throat when Bill approaches, and the others would straighten in their seats, swallow a time or two, lick their lips, and settle a blinking focus on whatever magazine is in their lap.

Like most days, Raincoat Woman is here again today. Although her hair is matted into wooly strands, she wears a reasonably new parka, and sits in an upright posture with a lap filled with magazines that she actually appears to read. She never relaxes enough to doze, alert to reposition when someone new joins or departs the clutch. She stands, studying the new geometry of bodies, and finds the seat that allows her the maximum personal space, as if some kind of magnetic polarity repulses her equally from all others. She pulls a chair out of formation to achieve the proper separation.

The regulars maintain disinterested peace whereas the auxiliary unfortunates sometimes grumble or argue. Carter saw a violent scuffle one time, quelled when Security Bill pulled the men apart with a firm hand on the back of each collar. Bill especially checks on Raincoat Woman a time or two each day, respectful of her tenure. At times she greets him with a worried look and a mumbled phrase that serves as an incoherent explanation. He leans over her shoulder. She holds Gourmet magazine toward him.

"Dutch baby," she says.

Bill nods with a flat smile. "Okay . . . sure." He turns to Carter and mouths: "poor thing."

Carter types: Dutch baby?

*

Forced inside to the place she now thinks of as "school" means Deidre has to be in the company of the men who drum at their machines. She is sympathetic to their suffering; bad stomachs or headaches, she assumes. They squint into their machines and then rub their faces and groan. She decides they may be getting shocked by the wires that feed from their smaller machines into each ear. They are drier and better-clothed than the Wet Ones, but they seem more distressed with life. Almost every Wet One reminds her of the men who sometimes steal her things from her secret nest near the freeway. She is not sure these are the same men, but who can tell? All wear stocking caps, denim pants frayed at the heals, and hide beneath so many layers of clothes that they can become different people by shedding skins.

A regular arrives, two plastic grocery bags of belongings in each hand, his giant blue shirt covered in large numbers, front and back. She waits for him to place his bags and take his seat before standing and relocating. As she measures the space in her mind, she can see the Squirrel watching over his glasses. He always watches. A dozen times a day he pulls a small bottle from his case, squirting liquid on his hands, and rubbing them together in a way she had seen squirrels "wash" in puddles in the park. She does not mind that he watches except that he acts as if he weren't watching, and when he raises his eyes over the top of his small glasses, it is the look of a man peeping over a back fence. He is feeding information on my movements into his machine, she thinks.

She looks at the slanted roof, a glass-and-steel honeycomb, and something about the way the lines and angles meet makes the static start. She checks her distance from the others. It doesn't seem right, and she pinches her eyes against the noise. She spreads her magazines like a hand of cards, looking for Popular Mechanics, and the story she once read about a gadget that makes electricity snap off when the sizzling gets too hot. Someone had implanted one in her head one night, she decided, because when her thoughts overheat now, some gizmo shoots her mind straight back to that morning, that last morning she made breakfast at home.

"Circuit-breaker," she says as Security Bill nears.

*

Carter taps the return key a few times to create a cumulus of white space at the bottom of his story, onto which he types a line from memory: "He was an old man who fished alone in a skiff in the Gulf Stream and he had gone eighty-four days now without taking a fish."

He types it again. And then recites it without sound, trying to will the rhythm into his mind. He tries to imagine the scene, but only sees Spencer Tracy in a movie. And every time he types the line, he is bothered that an editor did not split the sentence into two. If he had his way, it would read: "HAVANA, Cuba – Santiago, 75, broke his string of fishing futility at 85 days, although his marlin was denied consideration for the Gulf Stream record (18 feet) as it was eaten by sharks before he reached land." The Nobel Committee, Carter believes, had rewarded Hemingway for imprecise run-ons and a dreadful habit of burying his lead.

Carter had come to the library so regularly since the newspaper went out of business that he feels he should punch a clock. Everyone says the paper "folded," but that sounds like delicate origami rather than an economic atrocity. It disappeared in bite-like increments; workers pruned every quarter, the paper growing thinner and narrower, finally fading into the vanishing point. He presumed the only person who noticed the demise was the final subscriber, whom he imagined to be an eighty-five-year-old fisherman's widow in Ballard, who read the daily tidal reports out of fidelity to her long-dead husband.

With no job to occupy his time, he came to the library to write a memoir about a man who edited news stories for three decades before being emancipated to find his own voice. He wrote how the early rounds of layoffs were accompanied by solemn announcements and long-faced expressions of regret, but after half a dozen "Best Wishes" cakes, the regret seemed like artificially sweetened frosting, and employees just no longer showed up, as if they'd been edited out. Highlight-delete.

Security Bill started work at the library soon after Carter began his memoir. "Laid off? Me too," Bill said. "Foot patrol . . . West Precinct . . . Service, Pride, Dedication . . . pink slip."

After a few months working on his memoir, Carter showed several chapters to a former colleague, who suggested it lacked "narrative drive." Carter Googled a definition for "narrative drive" and decided his life lacked it as well. He conceded to his friend that a memoir might not "find its market," and that science fiction would be his new genre. He would carry the reader into the future, to a planet he created where newspapers were read by enlightened citizens; and those who wrote and edited the stories were considered heroic crusaders for noble expression.

"So . . . a humor piece?" his friend asked. He decided he needed to work at polishing his craft, and now works on short pieces filled with descriptions. He writes what he sees around him every day. He calls it "scene harvesting."

Raincoat Woman moves again. After triangulating position and distance, she sits fairly close to Carter. He looks over his glasses and inhales. Since she does not smell like the others, he considers the possibility that she is unkempt as a matter of personal style rather than hardship. Many in the Pacific Northwest affect that look. Maybe she isn't even homeless, but rather a "free-range" woman by volition. He retrieves his Purell bottle and doses his hands, working it between his fingers, and then raising his hands to his nose. He likes the sanitary smell.

*

Too close . . . too close to the Squirrel. When she looks at him, he drops his eyes back into his machine . . . updating her new coordinates. His nearness causes the static to rise to a higher pitch. Snap. Dutch baby . . . Dutch baby . . . that was what Sister Carmen called them in the Home Economics class all the girls were forced to take . . . so easy anybody could make them: Flour, eggs, butter . . . baked in an iron skillet . . . cinnamon and sugar on top. That's how she made them that morning for her step-father. Dutch babies . . . fat little pancakes. But they did not get eaten that morning. He made sure of it. She went to school anyway; straightened her plaid uniform skirt and went to school.

She closes her eyes to remember the smell of the Dutch babies that last morning before things happened and all the sizzling started. She remembers going to school anyway, to Sister Mary Francis's music class. The sister has a facial mole, but a pleasant voice. She sings a psalm and then teaches it to them. Sing it. Sing it again. Memorize it. You may need this some day, Sister Mary Francis tells them. Deidre needed it a great deal that very day. She sings it and never forgets it.

Over the static, she hums it now, and Bill draws near.

"Miry clay," she says, louder than normal. "Miry clay."

Bill turns to Carter. "Miry clay?" he says.

Carter likes the sound of the phrase. He Googles, The search takes time; the library needs better bandwidth, he thinks. It comes up: Psalm 40. He opens the entry.

"He brought me up out of a horrible pit, out of the miry clay, and set my feet on a rock, and established my goings."

Carter has never heard it. But he knows the feeling . . . slipping . . . slipping away . . . slipping toward a pit.

He reads the line to Security Bill. From memory, Deidre repeats it back to Carter, and sings it in a faint, wind-chime voice.

"What?" Security Bill asks.

Carter reads it again and Deidre joins so they are saying it together.

"Establish my goings," Carter says.

"Miry clay," Deidre responds, once to Bill, and then to Carter: "Miry clay."

Carter types it into his notes.

JOHN BUTLER

Sing this song with me – this is '40'

It is February 2012 in Dublin and I've just committed an act of reckless nostalgia, palming over nine euros to a lank-haired youth in a HMV T-shirt for a CD copy of *Under a Blood Red Sky*, recorded live at Red Rocks. It's for research purposes, but still; nine Jaysus euro?! It's been a while since I've bought a CD let alone one by U2, but when I first paid for this – on vinyl – around Christmas time in 1983, Golden Discs in Stillorgan charged me £5.99 and Ireland didn't even have a HMV. God, I sound old, and not for no reason. I turn forty in July.

Back to the music and okay, Prufrock, let us just forget all about coffee spoons for a minute, because the truth is I have measured out my life in U2 songs. This is not even a band that I love; frequently, in fact, I have hated them, and more often than not I've endured their output in the way you do a sandwich from an all-night garage. But the life of Irish man-folk of my vintage is never entirely extricable from that of our most renowned rock export. I haven't heard a note from U2's 1983 live album in well over two decades, but we came up together, and this CD will have the transportative qualities of a Tardis.

Back home, I take out the inlay card. As a child I spent so long poring over album sleeves looking for clues, and now fragments of memory swirl about before the music starts. How I tried to give myself a mullet with a Bic razor, hacking clumps from my scalp. The time I met the band, in my school uniform, and how I was mortified by that – as if they would have liked me more in my herring-bone denims. I remember also the general, great mystery of life beyond my tiny orbit, and then hooky, primitive, vaguely choral 'Gloria' kicks in; and folks, I am gone . . .

Back to 1982. The first time I am punched in the nose it is by a Bono-haired kid wearing a sleeveless *Boy* T-shirt, on a bright summer's day in the caravan park of a resort on the south-east coast of Ireland. I am ten and he is older, and there is something militaristic about his T-shirt; the flag, the font, the list of tour dates I read on the back as he walks away, fists still balled. I am intrigued by the music of my oppressor, because music, to me, is still owned by other people; the songs of Glen Campbell, Simon & Garfunkel and Abba beloved by other family members. But that is about to end. That evening in the chip shop, a swab of cotton wool in my nose, I pick a U2 song on the jukebox. I will follow.

Sing this song with me – this is '40'

'11 O'Clock Tick Tock' is a grey morning in 1984, when I'm sitting on a wooden bench in a corridor at the dingy Clarence Hotel, a drab block on the quays. U2 will later buy and restore this place, and I'll spend weekend nights of the Celtic Tiger 1990s in the bar wasting money and time. Now, though, I'm twelve years old, and waiting to do an interview, in Irish, to attend Irish college that summer in the Aran Islands. I'm listening to U2 on my Walkman when the interviewer comes out to call me in. Bearded and sweatered, he is ancient like Ronnie Drew. He hears lyrics leaking from my orange foam headphones and sternly informs me *as Gaelige* that English-language music is forbidden in Irish college. In a high-ceilinged smoky bedroom with a desk, behind which lies a concave mattress on a steel-framed bed, I pass the interview. He was probably forty.

'New Year's Day' is New Year's Day in 1985, in my parents' dining room in our old house. I insist on playing this song on repeat while my sister and I play snooker on our brand new 6x3 table. We have a half-size cue for shots closest to the wall, but still the rose-red walls are grazed with black rubber from the butt. At this point in their career, U2 are trying to emulate bands like Simple Minds and Echo and the Bunnymen, and Bono's accent is English; as is my apeing of it, into a snooker cue. The slate isn't true, shots to the corner pocket veering away from them, and I can feel the bumpy green baize, rougher and more wool-like than you'd find in a snooker club. This is the apotheosis of my U2 love.

By that summer I am quaveringly, self-loathingly pubic.

Mullets are out, and my body has begun its torment. I am investigating worlds of disguise and ironic detachment; cologne, polo necks, fake ID. The band storm Live Aid, playing 'Sunday Bloody Sunday' and 'Bad', and it remains the occasion on which I felt most proud to be Irish. My pride, however, is deeply conflicted because I have betrayed U2. They've become too big and popular; the older brothers of my friends abandoning their sincerity for the sideways-talking Violent Femmes, the impenetrable cool of the Velvet Underground and the ten-dollar chords of Aztec Camera. Blindly we follow suit, me bringing my vinyl copy of *Under a Blood Red Sky* into school, at lunch break swapping it for a frankly rubbish album by the Dream Syndicate. If I could have told my fourteen-year-old self it would be a quarter of a century before he heard the final track on *Under a Blood Red Sky* again, he would have snatched it back.

By now my world is splitting open into a million little pieces, the extent of what is out there almost dizzying to behold. There are so many books, so many places and so much unheard music that no one will again exert as singular an influence. But the shadow of this band is only lengthening. I meet Bono in a club in Dublin and cannot think of a single thing to say; so I say nothing, but not in a good way. I move to America and sell girls dresses in Macy's department store to a soundtrack of *Achtung Baby*. I get to see the band in San Francisco, then years later in Las Vegas. On the way back, flat broke, I stop off at Red Rocks. U2 have broken America, but we have begun our slide into different shades of uncertainty. In 2006, I watch a friend who had abandoned them back in school play 'The Electric Co.' to kids in a club in New York. Mullets are back, but I want to shout into the crowd that this is just an echo, and that they don't know what it was like. Instead, I retreat from clubs, into the night. The circle is closed.

Twenty-five years on and I'm listening to the closing song, '40', for the first time since the day of the school record swap. Forty. How is this landmark possible? By now, so many things were supposed to have happened in my life, and though some of them have, so many more have not! Thankfully, though, the metric by which we measure our life continues shifting. In school, we read the age of bubble-permed football players on Top Trumps cards and gave ourselves time. Later it was rock stars who had seen and done it all before expiring in bath-tubs at the age of twenty-seven. Thereafter, it became the Jesus Age, and they had strung him up on the cross by the time I owned my first car. Now, fresh horror as I learn that I've stepped past the age of Joyce's great flâneur – Leopold Bloom was thirty-eight the day he walked across Dublin. And Bono? By the time he hit forty he was already singing 'Beautiful Day'.

At the end of '40' the singer leaves the stage as the band plays on and the crowd keeps singing. Long ago, I was a boy singing into a snooker cue in Dublin, scanning record sleeves and trying to imagine what it could possibly be like – a live concert, a foreign country, the adult world. I have since been to Red Rocks and all points in between, and what has been lost, and gained, in the intervening years? U2's latest world tour has broken all records but I suspect that they'd swap a great deal of that money to arrest their slide into obsolescence – to get a finger in that dam really has no price. For me wonder, more than anything, is what has been lost since, and sometimes I think I would exchange all the memories of the things I have seen and done for the wonder of not knowing anything at all. More than anything, I miss mystery.

Back at Red Rocks, Adam Clayton leaves the stage, Edge leaves, then only Larry, the little drummer boy (all of twenty-three) remains, playing to a chorus from the crowd. 'I will sing, sing a new song'. What are the compensations, as four-oh enters my orbit; an enormous and menacing lump of interstellar rock speeding towards the dumbly revolving planet of my own existence? I am healthy, for one, as are those I love. I wrote a book I wanted to put my name to, and it found a home with a *simpatico* publisher before I – or they – reached forty. And as Larry leaves the stage to a standing ovation and the needle inches past forty, I console myself with one last thought – it is not yet time for forty-one.

SARAH BUTLER

Number 40

Melissa hated forgetting things. Wallet, umbrella, diary, keys – their absence always left her feeling anxious and unbalanced. Today it was her phone. She must have left it in the hallway on the table Simon bought last week, which she didn't like at all – dark varnished wood and spindly legs. He had bought it without consulting her, and when she'd started to say it wasn't to her taste, and that it would be great – now they were living together – if they could discuss such things beforehand, he'd looked so deflated she'd changed the subject.

She watched raindrops chase each other down the bus window. It was too late to turn back. She couldn't afford to miss the team meeting – it was hard enough getting noticed in that place, never mind promoted.

The bus stopped. People got off. People got on. Someone sat down next to her in a rustle of wet waterproofs, but

Melissa didn't turn her head. She looked instead out of the window at the pavement, which, when she narrowed her eyes enough to blur her vision, turned into a continuous grey line. This time last year they'd been in Santorini – a cluster of bright white buildings clinging to the remnants of a volcano; beaches that glittered with black sand. Melissa pictured Simon on their hotel balcony, sitting in a wide wicker chair, his calves tanned and muscular below khaki shorts, his eyes almost as blue as the sea way down at the bottom of the cliffs. She tried to think what the hotel had been called. She could picture the sign – hand-painted with a blowsy pink flower underneath the letters – but couldn't remember the name. If she'd had her phone she would have called Simon, because he was good at things like that. Do you remember Santorini? she'd say, and he'd laugh and say of course he did and didn't she wish they were there now, in that huge white bed; and she would curl her body further towards the window of the bus, make a cocoon for her phone with one hand, and talk just loud enough for him to catch the words. That, or he wouldn't answer, or he'd be distracted and rushed: what is it, Liss? She'd have to think of something banal and house-related to say; he'd be curt and she'd hang up wishing she hadn't called at all.

The team meeting didn't go well – not in any dramatic sense, it was more that Melissa suspected no one would have noticed if she had gone home to get her phone. At lunchtime she stood in the staff toilets and stared into the long mirror above the sinks. Underneath the fluorescent lights her face was pasty white. Even her hands, when she rubbed them against her cheeks to try and conjure up a bit of colour, looked like they'd been refrigerated. They needed another holiday; she'd say as much to Simon over dinner. He would point out that they'd agreed to wait until the house was done. Melissa was beginning to wonder what 'done' meant. The house had already endured eleven months of concerted attack – re-wiring, re-plumbing, re-plastering, re-painting, re-flooring. It's the dust, Melissa told herself, staring at her pale skin and dark eyes in the mirror. It's not good for someone to live with that much dust.

If it had been just her, she would never have bought the house – a tall, pompous terrace with stucco pillars propping up a shallow porch – but relationships were about compromise, and she was, at least, good at that.

It was still raining when she left the office. Commuters crammed into the bus, steaming up the windows, dripping water from their umbrellas onto the flecked vinyl floor. There was a woman standing by the door who reminded Melissa of that girl Simon worked with. They'd had her and her overbearing boyfriend round to dinner a month or so ago. It had been raining then too. Simon and Emma – or maybe it was Emily – went outside for a cigarette after they'd eaten. Watching them through the window, standing close together under the narrow porch, Melissa had felt suddenly cold and uncomfortable, as though she'd walked into an empty house that hadn't been lived in for years. The girl got off at Melissa's stop, and Melissa watched her clip down the street, resting a red umbrella against her shoulder like a parasol.

Melissa and Simon lived at Number 40 Rossendale Road, a three-and-a-half-minute walk from the bus stop. Theirs was one in a long line of terraced houses, on a street punctuated by trees which looked like they were shaking their fists at the sky. Melissa hunkered under her umbrella and tried to avoid the worst of the puddles. She was so busy thinking about the girl on the bus she didn't notice, straight away, that the house wasn't there.

In fact she walked up three white steps to a door which wasn't hers and shoved her key into the lock without paying much attention at all. The key didn't fit. She tried again, but the metal teeth jarred against the keyhole. And then she looked at the lock, and the door it was in, and realized that this door was pale grey, whilst their door was green – she had painted it herself. She let out a little huff of a laugh, retreated down the steps and walked up to the house on her right, but that door was also grey. And so she backed away and turned to the house on the left: yellow paint and with a thin silver knocker. You're losing your marbles, Simon would have said. Melissa imagined a stream of heavy glass balls, with twists of colour caught inside, falling onto the street and rolling down the shallow incline towards the main road.

After a year you'd think she'd remember where she lived. She knew she was on the right road, but she retraced her steps all the same until she reached the end of the terrace, and there, as she knew it would be, was the sign. Rossendale

Road. She lived at number 40 Rossendale Road. Melissa straightened her shoulders, and walked back towards her house. Quick, confident steps. She counted off the numbers: two, four, six, eight, 36, 38, 42.

Number 40 was not there.

There wasn't a hole where it used to be. There wasn't a fire-ravaged skeleton like she'd seen on the news plenty of times – people's intimate lives exposed to public view. There was simply nothing in between numbers 38 and 42 to suggest there ever had been a number 40.

Melissa closed her eyes. She counted to ten and then opened them again.

Number 40 was not there.

So she put down her umbrella, held both hands out in front of her and looked at them, because, right then, she wasn't sure if she was there either. They were pale but they looked real: slightly stubby fingers, neatly filed nails, the ring Simon had given her two weeks ago, over an intricate dinner of squid and scallops and king prawns, when she felt desperately sick but didn't have the heart to tell him. Three neat diamonds caught in three gold claws.

She needed to get inside and have a cup of tea. She needed a holiday. Melissa closed her eyes, took a deep breath, and looked again. A row of terraced houses: 36, 38, 42.

They hadn't met their neighbours. They'd left it too long after moving in, and it had got to the point where it would be embarrassing to just knock and introduce themselves. No one answered at number 42, but when she rang the bell of number 38 a man opened the door, in trainers, grey tracksuit bottoms and a blue T-shirt with patches of sweat underneath each arm.

'Yes?' There was an aggressive edge to his voice.

'I'm Melissa,' she said, and coughed. 'I mean, I live next door. That is—'

The man looked at her blankly. He scratched his side, lifting the hem of his T-shirt to show a pale belly dense with black hair.

'I'm looking for number 40,' she said.

'This is 38.'

'I know, I know that.'

'So you want next door.'

'But it's not there.'

She saw his nostrils flare. 'Look, love, this is 38.'

'And next door is 42,' Melissa said, trying to control her voice. 'Please, will you look?'

He eyed her suspiciously, but stepped outside. Melissa watched his face. His jaw moved in a chewing motion and she wondered if he ground his teeth in his sleep. He turned to her, lips pursed.

'Well, what do you know?' he said. 'I'd never noticed that.'

'But I live there,' Melissa said.

'In 42?'

'In 40.'

A lift and drop of the shoulders. 'I'd call the council then, if I was you.'

'It's gone six.'

'Stay with a friend then. I've got to jump in the shower.'

Melissa pictured her phone, sitting on the table in the hallway of number 40 Rossendale Road. Maybe, she thought, the table wasn't that bad after all. Maybe it was even something she could learn to love.

'Do you mind if I make a call?' she asked. 'I left my phone at—'

The man frowned, but nodded her inside and pointed to a grey house phone on a shelf crowded with pens and Post-it notes. When she picked up the receiver, Melissa realized she didn't know Simon's number. She always just scrolled down to his name on her mobile. She could find his office number though, this man must have the Internet. But then she looked at the man – who had pulled off his trainers and was regarding her impatiently – and she remembered, again, Simon standing next to that girl on the porch smoke billowing from their mouths, and she put the receiver down and walked out of number 38 and onto the street.

She sat on the pavement, in full view of the house that wasn't there any more. She couldn't remember if she'd drawn the living room curtains that morning, and now she came to think about it, she couldn't remember whether the bathroom window on the first floor had tiny stars or tiny squares etched into the glass. She stared at her umbrella, like a fallen bird at her feet, and watched the rain make dark pools in its folds.

She waited. And, long after the sun had set, and the rain had seeped through her coat and tights, she saw Simon, walking along the other side of the street. Her heart stirred and she was about to raise her hand and shout, when she saw he was on his mobile. Maybe he was leaving a message on her phone, which was still sitting on the table in the hallway of—. She turned; number 40 was still not there. And then she thought maybe he was talking to that girl – Emma or Emily. Instead of calling out to him, Melissa stayed where she was. They would laugh about this one day.

She watched as Simon approached where number 40 should be. She watched as he walked straight past number 38 and number 42 without so much as looking up from his phone. She hurried after him, past the end of the terrace and round the corner to a street where the houses stood in pairs, set further back from the road. He walked up to the front door of a house she didn't know, a house they didn't live in, and took a set of keys from his pocket.

'Simon!'

He turned, and she saw that it wasn't him at all. Similar, yes, but heavier around the face, with thinner, greyer hair; and she was pretty sure Simon would never wear a tie like that.

'I'm sorry,' she said.

He looked at her blankly and she backed away. As he opened the door, Melissa glanced into the hallway and saw, standing against the wall, a dark wooden table with spindly legs. The man who she thought was Simon closed the door. The rain started again, slow fat drops making join-the-dot patterns on the paving slabs. Melissa looked down at her hands, which were so pale they were almost translucent, and thought again of Santorini and those bright white buildings clinging to the rocks.

EMMA CHAPMAN

Forty Feet

There were forty new feet in the village. They came and went.

The thump of thick-heeled green boots marked the day. When it suited them, they approached the houses. They lined up empty outside when the soldiers took tea.

There were new footsteps in the night too, invisible and silent. Black rubber sandals, named for Ho Chi Minh, and known to all. Some came from the North, but some from the village itself. Under their day shoes, a few bore broad pale strap marks, a burden of long disappearances into the jungle. A sure sign of a communist, those feet were kept hidden, even from their neighbours.

Before, all doors were open and the people had laughed together. Now shadows crossed their faces, clouds falling across the cornflower blue of the mountains. They closed their doors, but somehow the sandals still crept in and watched them sleeping. Sometimes, they were invited, by old friends blind to new alliances.

The night belonged to the sandals. The dogs heard them passing and barked into the black. A crack of wood or a wet splash near the river. The shifting paddy fields were alive under the silver moonlight.

Inside their homes, people shut their ears and eyes against the whoosh of tracers and whirr of helicopters, which broke through their sleep and had them swatting the air. Like the dogs, they had their warnings: white towels hanging on the line, or a bottle in the window, telling the sandaled feet when to stay away.

When the roosters called, it was safe. The place was theirs again. As the green light spread, they slipped on their shoes and went out into the fields. Occasionally, they met boots coming back, or lying in the long grasses, the sounds of snoring like buffalo. They were becoming lazy: there were fewer sandals since the tall men had moved in.

As the sun spread heat, the market started with flashes of colour and sound. The tall white men slept at the end of a canopied lane. They had taken over a huge ancient house on stilts, digging a trench and surrounding it with angry silver coils of wire. The stilts had been to keep the old owners safe from wild animals, but now the space underneath was a store for weapons and a makeshift bar. Around the base were coconut trees and the beginnings of a disused coffee plantation. The land beyond felt forgotten, overgrown with countless shades of green.

After lunch, there was silence and stillness. In the shadowy rooms, the villagers rested. The tall men woke and got hungry, pulling on their boots and kicking dust clouds through the lanes.

When *Mistar For* stood up, they said his head grazed the heavy clouds. His long shadow fell across the houses and blotted out banana trees, but he also had the whitest teeth, shown often. They were not afraid.

Mistar Akin was shorter and wider. He walked with his hand on his gun. Dark hairs peeped from his shirt, and he had a bristling moustache like a caterpillar. He laughed less often, watching Mistar For first.

For the soldiers, the boots were a nuisance. They were tight and uncomfortable, making their skin itch. And they made too much noise in the night.

In the warm afternoon air, the men did not need to whisper.

'I'm still half asleep, Ford,' the shorter man said.

'Cold beer will sort that. That, or Missy Kieu.'

He laughed. 'Sight for sore eyes. Right now I'd take the beer.'

They stopped outside a low wooden house with a thatched roof. Leafy vines hung over the front wall, and butterflies hovered. The men could smell something meaty cooking. The front gate creaked. 'Hello there?' they called out.

From the dark interior came Missy Kieu, her black hair

tied in a braid. Her skin was smooth and pale; her eyes grey, her hands wet from the sink. She smiled and gestured to three low stools in the shade.

The men stooped and sat like ungainly insects. A hen and her chicks pecked around their feet; a small dog ran yapping under a tree with a twisted trunk. Missy Kieu went inside and Ford unlaced his boots, slipping off his socks and rubbing his bare feet. Atkins copied him.

Far off, they could hear children laughing.

'It's so quiet here,' Ford said. 'You can about imagine it's paradise.'

'Except it isn't.'

'Humour me, Atkins. I didn't get much sleep.'

'Just don't be getting too relaxed.'

Ford poked him. 'You need to get laid.'

Missy Kieu came back outside carrying a bowl of small brown things, keeping her eyes down. Ford took one and put it into his mouth. It crunched between his teeth.

Atkins followed. 'What the hell is this?'

'How would I know? Just smile and be polite.' Ford nodded his head and rubbed his belly.

Missy Kieu grinned. She raised her hands, slowly cupping a blue butterfly. There was a faint fluttering against her palm. She pinched the wings and held them still, pointing between the trapped creature and the bowl. She did it again.

'What's she trying to tell us?' Atkins asked.

'I don't care, I just like watching her move.'

Missy Kieu opened her fingers and let the butterfly free.

Pointing after it, she picked up a small brown husk between her fingers and held it out to them.

'I haven't the faintest,' said Ford, smiling and popping another one into his mouth. 'But these sure grow on you.'

There was the hiss of beer cans opening. A regular beat of knife hitting board started through the open doorway, and pots clanged. Gentle humming stopped and started. Atkins lit a cigarette. The men sipped.

Missy Kieu pointed at the low surface between them.

'Ta-bel,' she said.

Ford nodded and smiled. 'Table.'

She pointed at an empty stool. 'Char.'

'Chair.'

Missy Kieu's plump lips mimicked his, over and over, and he blushed.

A man appeared, smiling, his face creased with sleep. He brought more beers and some strange fruit, spiky like pink and green horse-chestnut shells, fussing at his daughter in sharp Vietnamese. 'Wel-come,' he said to the men. 'Make self home.'

Ford grinned. Atkins smoked, then flicked open his knife, slitting open the shells and popping the white fleshy fruit into his mouth. The smooth insides of the shell made him think of clacking conkers and his brother's eyebrows furrowing.

Mr Quan's wife came out of the house carrying two steaming bowls: rice and a stew, the chunks of yellow fat glistening. Missy Kieu handed the men chopsticks, and they all ate together, sitting around the tiny table. The men let the foreign language fall around them as their hosts chatted, and Ford could almost imagine what it would be like if they were not there at all.

After dinner, the plates were cleared, more beer was opened, and Mr Quan re-emerged with a guitar, missing a string, the body scratched and bloated from the sun.

He handed it to Ford, who played haphazardly, popular songs from back home, his voice loud but tuneless. Missy Kieu hummed along. After a while, Mr Quan nodded and reached for the guitar. Cradling it, his brown fingers moved easily along the frets. Atkins felt himself close his eyes, immobilized by the music and beer. He was back in the little blue boat back home, floating, looking up through the sunlight dappled trees. Neither of the men could have said later how long he played for, but they walked back to the base in a daze.

That night, Ford and Atkins were on patrol again. They walked down the deserted lanes with two muttering Vietnamese police soldiers.

'I wish they'd shut up,' Atkins said. 'They're going to give us away.'

Ford only put his finger to his lips, the whites of his eyes glimmering in the moonlight. They had heard reports of the communists using sampans in the river, and they waited amongst the sugar cane by the bank, their guns ready. As the night wore on, they heard and saw nothing, and their guns began to droop. Several times, one had to wake the others.

When the sun skimmed the dark mountains, throwing a soft yellow light across the paddy fields, Ford signalled to the men and they rose slowly, stretching their legs and backs. They walked back through the narrow dirt roads bordered by trespassing green. Ahead, a shadow: Missy Kieu's father, moving across a thicket into his back garden.

'Morning, Mr Quan,' Ford called out. Mr Quan froze, his shoulders lifting. Slowly, he turned around. Then he smiled.

'Mistar For.'

He turned back.

'What's he doing out before sunrise?' Atkins said.

'He's probably getting ready for market.'

'I've got a bad feeling, Ford.' He paused, looking back. 'He's wearing the sandals.'

'Atkins, it's Mr Quan: we know him.'

'We don't know any of these gooks. Not really.'

'Don't talk about them like that. We were at his house this afternoon. He gave us—'

There was the sharp whistle of something behind them, and Ford was on his knees. His face and eyes whitened and his mouth fell open as his cheek moved towards the sandy path. Atkins ducked down beside him. On the ground was the back of his head. He picked it up, wet and sticky, and tried to put it back. Turning him over, Atkins saw Ford's eyes were open and flat, and he thought of the fish his father would bring home from the green river.

He looked around but he could see only the long grasses, the stretching coconut trees, and there, crouched trembling in the dust, the two Vietnamese soldiers they had patrolled with, their faces hidden behind their hands.

'Get help, for Christ's sake,' Atkins roared, and then he was on his feet, pushing past the men as he headed back down the path, the trigger cold under his finger.

The lane was quiet and the normal far-away sounds of the crowing cocks and buzzing cicadas made his skin itch. He waited, but could hear no movement. Knowing where to go, he moved cautiously, his gun ready. Alone now, his boots took him back the way they had come, the mingling greens blurring at the edges of the path. When he reached the fence to Mr Quan's house he jumped over it, ducking down behind a clump of waist-high cassava plants. Through the arrow-shaped leaves, he saw two figures bent towards each other like question marks: Mr Quan, and a man wearing black pyjamas.

Atkins raised his gun. Pointing it through the leaves, he fired. The man in black fell without making a sound, and Mr Quan turned to flee around the side of the house. Atkins fired two more shots as he ran after him. When he reached the crumbling wall of the house, he paused, holding his lighter up to the edge of the thatch and blowing gently until it caught, the flames licking up the rice straw.

Then he ran on, down the orange earthen path between the houses, dodging past people starting their day, their eyes widening when they saw him, gun ready. Mr Quan was up ahead, and Atkins pushed on, feeling his brow prickle with sweat. He wished he could call for back-up, but they hadn't even taken the damn radio.

Gaining ground, he lined up Mr Quan's right leg in the sight. The familiar metallic click and bang and he saw the man fall like a deer, crying out. He pulled himself up, dragging his body forward, but soon Atkins was upon him, pressing his own hand into the wound until he cried out. The sound made him forget Ford's brain all covered in dust.

Taking him by the shoulders, he dragged him back to the base and left him with the Vietnamese police. They said that Ford's body was being picked up from the clearing. As he walked away through the jungle, he could hear Mr Quan's screams, though he could not understand his words. He wondered if he would tell them anything they didn't already know. He wondered if they would kill his daughter.

The helicopter was coming in to land, hovering over the coconut trees and throwing up wind. The medics were waiting with the body bag. Atkins unzipped the bag and put his hands on Ford's chest, reaching for his ID tag.

Pulling out his legs, he removed the boots. The sight of Ford's socked feet made Atkins's face wet. Then he zipped up the bag and walked away, the boots hanging from his hand by their laces. Above the line of trees, he could see a thick plume of grey smoke rising from the direction of the village.

Later that day, they hung Mr Quan's battered body from the ankles in front of the base, the pale crosses staining his skin as if he had been marked out.

KATE CLANCHY

A Judgement

In this story, you have a particular friend. You've known her a long time – since college, at least, but probably even earlier. Maybe you smoked Consulate out the window of the sixth-form library together. Maybe you went to primary school together, shared a desk, a pot of poster paint, an obsession with French plaits.

The point is, she's always been your high-achieving friend, the one whose exam results were always that bit better than yours, distinctions to your merits, A* to hard-won A. She's that bit more glamorous than you, too: a size down in jeans, hair naturally curly or naturally straight, whichever is in fashion the year you turned seventeen. No spots, no fillings. And this may have been bit hard, over the years, but no one could say she isn't loyal. When she got asked to the school dance, or prom, depending on your generation, and you didn't, by the boy you fancied, she insisted he took both of you, for instance, and that was kind however badly it all turned out. And it was also nice that she wanted you to be her bridesmaid, even if weddings aren't your thing, and maroon is nobody's colour.

Anyway, by the time you are both thirty-five, partnered up, and pregnant, she has this really good job. The job is very important to the question you will be asked at the end of the story, so please, apply your imagination to it strenuously. The job has an excellent salary and very long hours, but it should only be in banking if that's the sort of job you admire and are in yourself, the sort that you really approve of. Otherwise, make her the head of an important charity, fighting for civil rights, relieving famine, something like that. Or, if you're the arty sort, have her succeed in the area you most admire: make her a film-maker of rare and glorious distinction, or a theatre director, the nation's finest, something on that level. And give her husband the just-same sort of job, but ten years senior and even more demanding and well-paid. He's her first boss: a very much top-drawer type, driven, a bit distant, very trim and elegant. Your partner is your college boyfriend and he usually has egg on his trousers. He also has round shoulders, and enthusiasms so boundless you sometimes worry they are random. As for your job, I'm afraid you've just lost it. Yes. Redundant when pregnant – that old story, but cleverly done. Don't even think you could sue.

At least the redundancy means, though, that when your baby is three months old, there is no question of going back to work. Because, let's be honest, they wouldn't let you through the door. You're at least three stone overweight, and still walking funny and wetting yourself after the emergency caesarean. Your breasts are cushion-size, and leak, especially the left one. You have forgotten what it is to sleep at night, and despite all the breast milk, your baby has eczema so bad you are deprived of all compensatory baby prettiness and silkiness and general admiration – old ladies stooping to look in your pram jump back, repulsed. Your house is a mess, your confidence at an all-time low.

Your friend comes round. She says the Pilates really helped her through her water birth, and definitely with getting back in shape since. She shows you her baby, slender, muscular, and bright-eyed as kitten, and the tiny creature meets your eyes and smiles. Andrea. Your friend is enlarging on her future plans. She has hired a nanny. She was dealing with work documents within a few hours of the birth, and now she is going back full-time. Andrea is ten weeks old.

'What about the breast-feeding?' you squeak, for you are preoccupied with feeds and how you could possibly get the baby to have his main one in the day, not the night.

'I moved over to bottles,' she says, coolly. 'She's had her six weeks.' You say nothing, but you eye up her neat blouse and find yourself chewing over this pronouncement, often, during the next few months, especially when you have the mastitis, and when you switch to the millet-only diet, the one you find does nothing for the eczema or your figure. At La Leche, you make a new friend, a solid, militant Finn called Ulli, and confide in her about your old pal with the nanny. 'It is horrible!' says Ulli. 'The child will have no antibodies! She will not bond with her mother! She will grow up with a hole in her brain.' Which is what you'd hoped she'd say.

But little Andrea has skin like a rose petal, and she is very well bonded with her nice, intelligent, well-paid, permanent nanny, who you see in the park frequently, who takes Andrea to music class and baby gym already. The nanny keeps you up with the milestones: Andrea smiles, crawls, walks, runs, hops, and speaks earlier than your child, and better. At Andrea's second birthday party – to which you are invited, for you are never forgotten – her mother says to you, 'You mustn't think I don't admire you for doing it all yourself: I really think that's a wonderful choice. But I just couldn't do the, you know, animal, vegetable bit. The farming bit. For me I find that now Andrea is speaking, we can really form a relationship. I'm finding she's such a great person.'

You're pregnant again, at this point, the shape of kohlrabi. You are still untidy and disorganized and poor and you are increasingly bad-tempered. The toddler is a fussy eater, and you are inclined to feed him baked beans and white bread, and then feel angry with yourself about it. It is impossible to say that Andrea is disadvantaged in any way by having her nanny feed her on fresh vegetable soup, dried apricots, and pomegranate juice. She is starting the violin. It is impossible to say what is good about your choice, this mucky, short-term, animal life which seems to have been going on for ever, this round of viruses and exhaustion and E45 cream which the child will not even remember. You call Ulli, and she tells you that the first three years with a child are psychologically the most valuable, and throws in a sad story about neglected monkeys making bad mothers. You decide to solve the problem by not seeing your friend any more, or at any rate, not till you've got your figure back, which is the same thing.

But you underestimate her, her kindness, perceptiveness, loyalty. When you have the second baby she comes round with gifts, she arranges several days out with Andrea and the nanny for your peeling, be-spectacled, and now extremely jealous and angry toddler. She says she is quite sure that all children bite. She says she wishes she had another child, but that genuinely, she does not have the time and the resources, and this sounds to you like a true and regretful and also admirably self-knowing statement. She holds your baby with real tenderness, and when he is six weeks old, she sets you up with a little bit of freelance work you can do from home.

Which definitely helps. Whatever Ulli says. A bit of contact with the adult world, emails marked important (!), arriving for you. You even stagger into the office and make a small presentation, squeezed into a three-year-old jacket, and feel lifted by it. It's all easier, anyway, the second time around. The baby has a lovely nature, or maybe it's just not having eczema, or just that you're not so crap at the whole thing, any more. You start the toddler at nursery three days a week, take on another small job, don't see Ulli so much, and when you hear that Andrea is starting prep school, that she can play the flute, when you receive letters actually written in her four-year-old hand, you manage genuinely to be pleased. You say to Ulli, 'I really think that as feminists we need to respect each other's choices,' and tune out when Ulli starts on about the class aspect of life in England, and how the longer she lives here, the less she can stand it.

In fact, by the time your hit your fortieth year, your friendship is so happy, and so calm and centred and even a bit thinner are you, that when your old friend scores a huge triumph in her job, makes headline news, and starts to work part-time in Paris, you are thrilled, and defend her to your partner, who is having a weirdly conservative moment. Her work is a true inspiration. It shows how women can work better after childbirth, and besides, your friend is at home with Andrea every weekend. They have carefully defended quality time, and sometimes you are asked to join them. When your birthday rolls round, you have no problem with inviting the whole set, mother, father, daughter, and nanny to your actually rather laborious get-together in a youth hostel in the Brecon Beacons.

They're frightfully nice about it. They drive all sorts of places, and the nanny looks after ten children so you can go to the pub. Andrea and her mother are great together, even though the kid has a cold or something – easier, really, than you and your still-itchy, still-mulish, still not specially-bright older son, and over the third pint in the Welsh pub you think, OK, let her have it. The job, the kids, the money, cheers, my friend. And you toast her, over your messy glass. You don't say anything, of course, but your friend must sense your change of heart, because it is to you that she turns just a few weeks later, your messy kitchen in which she suddenly appears, incongruous in her silk shirt and suit.

This is the story. In the last few months, Andrea has been getting clumsy. The nanny noticed it, and the teachers. She's been dropping things – balls, toys; she's been finding it harder and harder to hold a pen, she has found it very difficult to get dressed. When she walks, she stomps, on her heels. Recently, her speech, always so clear, has seemed slurred, especially when she's tired. In school, she puts her head on the desk, says she has forgotten words she has been able to read for years, sleeps. Both your friend and her partner have loads of health insurance, and so the nanny has taken the child on a round of medical appointments. And now they have a diagnosis and this is it.

Andrea has an incurable, degenerative, genetic disease of the nervous system: something like Huntingdon's but much more unusual. An ataxia. A rare variant. Your friend repeats the name of the disease and the number of its variant several times, but you can't take it in. You're thinking: my child stomps. And: is it catching? You need to stop that, and drag your mind back to Andrea. What is happening is: her brain cells are dying and not renewing themselves. This is the prognosis: progress will be rapid. Andrea will be in a wheelchair in three months, quadriplegic in a year, unable to swallow in eighteen months, and unable to breathe (dead) within two years.

Now you are thinking: if Andrea has it, my kids can't get it. Stalking horse, scapegoat, sacrificial kid. Then you think about Andrea: clever little Andrea cross-legged on the floor, reading a book, and you imagine the words swimming in front of her eyes, the wobble in the legs, the hands, and you want to throw up. You sit down at your kitchen table and take your friend's hands. She is still talking about the diagnosis. What happens is: the cerebral cortex dies first. Andrea will lose her speech and her higher intellectual functioning before she loses the rest of it. Probably in the next three months. So, by the time she is reduced to animal level, being spoon-fed in a cradle, she won't know it. That must be a mercy. When she's back in nappies, she won't know who's changing them. Animal vegetable. Farming. A body. The nanny has said she will stay on.

You pour your friend a whisky, and one for yourself. It's three in the afternoon. Your hands are shaking. And here comes the question. It's about the job. Your friend has three months' compassionate leave, but after that, she needs to be back in Paris, because after that the project will die. Should she give up her job? She's really asking. For the first time in your long history, she doesn't seem to have worked out the answer in advance. So, what do you think?

Yes, that's the instinctive response, but think about it a

bit more. Engage your brain, the way she always does, the way you don't. Why do you think that? Why her? Why now? Who benefits?

Now, open your mouth and tell her. Tell her why.

HOWARD CUNNELL

Forty Metres Down

Forty metres down in the cold, dark Baltic Sea, off the Hel Peninsula, Poland, feels as deep as forty miles. This is a dive into non-existence. The blackness that surrounds me is so complete I don't experience it as water, but as absence. Somewhere nearby is a World War Two German E-boat. Just moments before I'd swum straight into it, but now I can't find it again in the consuming darkness. I forget the wreck, the reason I'm here. From all directions the cold spears right through me, numbing my lips – exposed and clamped down on my regulator's mouthpiece – and biting into my gloved fingers. I need to get me and my buddy Nick out, but I'm fighting a feeling beyond panic. An increasing disconnect. A remoteness from everybody I love up on the surface world. My girlfriend and children seem impossibly far away. I know that if I just give in, accept this remoteness and stop this struggle in the dark, then the terror will be over, and I'll be gone. The first clear thought in a long time: I might not make it out of here.

More than ten years have gone since that dive in the Baltic, but it's never far from my mind, especially when I get together with Nick. I'm sure we don't always mean to talk about it, but after a few beers, and if there's no one else around, it's likely we'll go over it once again. There are obvious reasons why we do this. We are divers, and divers love to tell stories about dives that go wrong, and no dive could have gone more wrong, unless we hadn't come back.

I was a professional diver then, and my friend still is, so there's a need to break down the component parts of the day and the dive, to isolate and name the many mistakes we made. Mistakes that began in a waterfront bar the night before, if we're being honest. We need to do this because, panicking and narcotized in the lancing cold and near-perfect darkness of deep water, illuminated only by the feeble and refracted light streams from our torches, it was impossible to know or understand what the other was experiencing. I did not know, for example, that almost as soon as he was in the water, the heavy rope Nick was carrying had become wrapped around his legs.

Mostly, though, I think we keep going over it because we haven't yet been able to say how it really was. There always comes a point, most often late in the night when the rum bottle has been opened, when we try and fail to tell one another how it felt to be so close to dying. I can't speak for Nick, but it feels important to try and find the words. If I don't, then a part of me will always be terrified and alone, forty metres deep in the bitingly cold darkness, with the awful weight of all that water bearing down on me.

At the time, I ran a small dive company and I was always looking for new places to dive – the more off the beaten track the better. A good friend of mine, Steve, a softly spoken, angular, quietly obsessive diver with a lovely Polish wife, came to me with an idea. His brother-in-law, Kuba, a diver and lifeguard living in Warsaw, had told Steve about a town called Hel, on the coast near Gdansk that was a wreck-diver's paradise, undived by anybody but a handful of locals. We bought a chart. There were wrecks everywhere. Mostly from World War Two of course: submarines, destroyers, E-boats, sculptural rusted hulks sunk to block the harbour from U-boats. Kuba had dived the sites with his friend Krystof, and he said that they would drive down from Warsaw with tanks and a compressor and meet us in Hel. Steve's wife Eva found us somewhere to stay. Kuba was in touch with a man who had a boat.

We quickly booked the trip out. Including me there were eight divers. Eva acted as interpreter. Kuba, twenty-one, a tall, serene skinhead who listened to hardcore punk music the whole time, and Krystof, a charming and elaborately moustachioed diving instructor, looked after us. People who were on that trip say they've never forgotten it. Partly because we were going into uncharted territory and making things up as we went along – which was really the whole point of what I wanted to be doing. These days when you book a dive trip you pretty much get your hand held from the minute you get off the plane. I wanted something a bit more adventurous. Poland was certainly that, and I should have been really excited and up for it, but to be honest, I was mostly distracted and hungover the whole trip. A deadly combination for a diver.

For a while after we got there it looked like there wouldn't be any diving. The weather was bad and the skipper and his boat were stuck in Gdansk. The wind howled and the rain fell heavily for a night and a day. Krystof took us down to the beach to curse Poseidon. We stood swearing loudly with our backs to the cold grey rolling sea. We threw vodka over our shoulders – a drink for Poseidon, to stop the strong winds blowing. The next day the weather cleared, but we were having trouble getting our tanks pumped. The Russian submarine compressor Krys and Kuba had brought down from Warsaw kept blowing all the fuses in the town. Finally, we loaded the compressor onto Kuba's trailer and drove it round to the kitchen of the restaurant where we took our meals, and managed to fill the tanks.

In the morning we went down to Jastarnia harbour and met our boat – the *Atosza* – and Arek, her skipper. For the next couple of days we dived on wrecks in horribly cold water with almost no visibility. The best site was Torpedownia – a torpedo-research centre off the coast of Gdynia. The morning we dived her she appeared out of the fog like the ruined temple of some long forgotten civilization, standing about a hundred feet proud of the sea. She was covered in graffiti, four-sided, almost like a concrete derrick, and you could see two torpedo chutes in the centre. We swam down the chutes, and there were still intact torpedoes on the sea floor.

The next day Arek took us to a deep wreck he'd discovered, a still unnamed E-boat, which lay in forty metres of water. He wanted us to take a heavy line down and tie it on the wreck so that our divers wouldn't pull down the light shot-line. Nick and I had argued late into the night that this wasn't necessary. All our divers carried a submersible marker buoy and a reel. The SMB is simply an inflatable bag that the diver can send up from depth to mark his position in the water. On wreck dives boat skippers put down a weighted line, called a shot-line, as close to the dive site as possible. A good skipper will put the shot right on a wreck. The diver then descends the shot-line. You can ascend up the shot-line too – and that's probably the best way to come up because it means you surface close to the boat – but we were used to sending up SMB's and coming up where we wanted. At home, it was never a big deal for the dive boat to come to you and pick you up. Wreck dives, drift dives, reef dives: it was standard practice to put up a blob, surface under, and wait for the boat to come and get you.

Because the surface visibility was so bad, with lots of fog, Arek insisted on anchoring over the wreck site. So, if you didn't come up either the shot-line, or the heavy line he wanted us to take down and tie onto the wreck, you were in for a swim back to the boat, or a long wait at the surface, at best. Nick said that the viz was so bad in the water, it was almost inevitable that divers wouldn't work their way back to the lines. For us, the safest way to dive the wreck would be to go down the shot, and come up under a blob. For the skipper, putting up an SMB meant something had gone wrong.

I don't know what I was trying to prove. Things were not good at home and maybe that's why I was behaving badly. I should have done what I was told instead of letting myself get distracted. This was Arek's boat and Arek's water, and that was all I really needed to know. Nick and I kitted up in silence. Fog surrounded us and crept in beneath the little tarpaulin canopy we stood under. We backrolled over the side, and Arek handed down the heavy rope to Nick. From the start, I was all wrong in the water, and not in control. The black descent was a long fall down. Pressure squeezed my ears and my suit against my body. I was being crushed. Nick kept crashing into me and I couldn't work out why. His air bubbles crowded against my face. I shone my torch against my computer to check my depth. I couldn't make any sense of it. My computer had frozen on the previous dive and I borrowed another diver's spare. The borrowed computer was configured to feet, not metres. The numbers were three times higher than I'd expected, and for a few terrifying seconds, I thought I was over ninety metres deep. When I finally crashed down, there was a huge dead white fish, belly up, at the bottom of the shot line; the fish almost luminous in the darkness, and rocking gently on its spine from side to side. Nick was making signs at me I didn't understand. I swam blindly around and smashed head first into the wreck. The water became granular as we kicked up the bottom. I lost control of my fear. Death came for me in a cold rush.

Ahead of me, but close, I saw a thin, fuzzing frame of light – exactly as though I was in a black room looking at a shut door behind which was another, lighted room. This was not the light of heaven that you hear people talking about, but the light of nothing. I think now that I was so close to passing out that I could see what unconsciousness would be like. I knew that the light was my death, and it was then I saw my two-year-old daughter's tawny face, her lion-coloured hair frizzed out. I wanted to see her again, and I knew that if I didn't stop drifting towards the death-light I wouldn't. Maybe my daughter saved me. Maybe Nick made contact. I do know that suddenly we were facing each other. I wonder if he saw the same look of terror in my eyes as I saw in his. Together we signalled, up, and began the slow ascent to the surface, to the light and the sweet air.

All the way home the only thing I could think about was how I was going to tell my girlfriend that I'd nearly died. Even if I couldn't tell it properly, when she saw how scared I still was, she'd know that this was not just another story. She wasn't there, and the next day she told me I had to leave. She was sick of me always going away. She said that even when I was home I was not present. I know, I said. I understand that now. It's too late, she said. What could I do? She was right. I left, carrying the death story inside me.

That summer I worked as a lifeguard in an open-air pool, and saved my wages. I slept at the pool or on a friend's floor and saw my kids when I could. I had a brief affair with a tall, strawberry blonde nineteen-year-old girl who worked at the pool, and who had skin the colour of honey. In October I flew out to Mexico, and arrived in the village of San Augustinillo in November.

I spent some months in that little village in Mexico. I lived under a palm tree a stone's throw from the Pacific's shoreline, and all my possessions fit in one bag. I dived for fish and sold them to restaurants. I was trying to figure out what mattered. I'd learnt that life can end at any moment, but knowing that made it harder to make decisions, not easier. As always when I am by the sea, I was home, but the woman I'd lost represented home, too. What I decided, sitting on that beach, was that the sea would always be there for me, but the woman would not. I got a plane back. I had no reason to think that we could get back together, but in time we did.

I would like to say, that having felt death come by so closely, I have learned how best to live a life that can end at any time. But beyond simply trying to be present, and attentive to each moment, I'm not sure that's true. Too often it seems that I am still falling through the dark, but I can say that the right person is holding my hand.

EDWARD DOCX

Great novels that I have loved . . . in 40 words

1. *The Great Gatsby*
F. Scott Fitzgerald

Beautiful people were everywhere visible in the lighted windows of the great house beyond – dancing, drinking, damned.

"Gee, I bet you're not really from Oxford," Nick drawled.

"Am so," said Gatsby, affecting a grandeur that did not quite ring true.

2. *Lolita*
Vladimir Nabokov

Ladies and gentlemen of the jury, had I been a painter, you would have seen a dolorous nymph asleep in her flame-flowered arbour, wearing a single sock, while callipygian cherubim climbed columns of onyx and birds of paradise gently wept.

3. *The Unbearable Lightness of Being*
MILAN KUNDERA

After the talk with the man from the ministry, Tomas fell into a deep depression. Unsure about Beethoven, Dionysius or kitsch, he visited Sabina. She put on a bowler hat and then stripped to her underwear. This cheered him up.

4. *Middlemarch*
GEORGE ELIOT

"I married because I was intellectually infatuated," asserted Dorothea Brooke, somewhat stubbornly.

"I married because I was physically infatuated," replied Dr Lydgate, somewhat regretfully.

"Well, such is English provincial life and you're both very immature," concluded George Eliot, somewhat chidingly.

5. *Crime and Punishment*
FYODOR DOSTOYEVSKY

After much deliberation, Raskolnikov, a much conflicted student, stole into an old lady's apartment and there murdered her with an axe. Though undetected, he was rather shaken and fell into a fever during which he sought the company of policemen.

6. *Wuthering Heights*
EMILY BRONTË

"Cathy, I know that my eyebrows meet but you must marry me instead of Edgar," Heathcliff cried out, like a beast wrenched in agony from its life-long mate.

"Let me alone," Cathy sighed with a petulance she would later regret.

7. *For Whom the Bell Tolls*
ERNEST HEMINGWAY

The Spanish sun was hot. I'm going to blow that bridge if it kills me, Robert thought. The Spanish sun was still hot. But Robert crawled towards the bridge under fire. And blew it up. And it did kill him.

8. *Metamorphosis*
FRANZ KAFKA

Painfully, he waited in the room without anything decisive happening. His father was unhappy. His mother was hysterical. His sister was adamant he must be got rid of. There was nothing to be done. He sank his head and died.

9. *Heart of Darkness*
JOSEPH CONRAD

"Let me tell you how I went up the Congo looking for a man named Kurtz," said Marlow.

"Why?" asked everyone else.

The solemn sky grew darker until the light was extinguished and only the sound of the river remained.

10. *Pride and Prejudice*
JANE AUSTEN

"Your expectations will be answered," she said, her colour heightening despite the most resolute composure of countenance. "But I implore patience. Though the truth may indeed be universally acknowledged in advance, we are nonetheless required to arrive there by increment."

11. *The History of Tom Jones*
HENRY FIELDING

Tom awoke in a strange bed beside a young lady of his most recent acquaintance . . . But here, dear reader, we must break away to the bosom of Sophia Western where, at this very moment, calamity pressed hard its exertions.

12. *Anna Karenina*
LEO TOLSTOY

Anna shared a train carriage to Moscow with Vronsky. It was intense. The same again on the overnight home. It was even more intense. And now – uh oh – she finds her husband repulsive because his ears press against his hat.

WILL EAVES

We Are Prey

Forty days and nights among the faithful

Note

In the spring of 1995 I spent forty days and nights in the states of Louisiana, Alabama, Mississippi, Texas, and New Mexico. What follows is an accurate, but not factual, recollection: a retrieval of voices, opinions, and responses heard at the time. The many encounters were largely (though not always) informal, the conversations various, often returning to matters of religious belief and self-determination. Throughout the Bible, the number forty denotes a period of time – it may be years, it may be days – in which rain falls, a difficult journey is undertaken, wisdom rules, a man starves, or a generation passes.

WE

Darryl

"I wouldn't be without him, of course. Today we drove out across the Pontchartrain Bridge to the north shore. Vera's, it's a wonderful seafood restaurant. I had the gumbo and Curtis had the blackened catfish. He said I should 'get wild' and go to Bourbon Point. Well, be that as it may, on the way back we took a detour to the NASA facility, where they have the Saturn 5 first-stage rocket on its side, like something from a giant forest? A petrified forest. They never used it, or we wouldn't be able to see it. Five massive burners out at the back and all that rigging, all the pipes and bolts snaking around the base of the rocket. I started to wonder what the moonshots had been for – and then I chanced to look up, and there he was, the man in the moon, staring down at me between two of the burners. I'm not saying he hasn't many, many faults, but he's happy and that's all that – and he's reliable, except – *here* he comes! Moose! Moose! C'm here! Moose isn't my dog, you understand. I'm *his* owner."

Evelyn

"I've been involved with clinic defense for years now. Agitation is flaring up because two fundamentalist activists have just been released from jail. One guy was locked up for non-payment of child support. He doesn't believe in birth control or after-care, apparently. The other is Randall Terry, the diehard who sent the President an aborted foetus in a pickling jar. Right. And they want the clinics closed down, that's what Operation Rescue is aiming for. Actually I think they want us all dead, but you know, start small and work your way up. I have some OR next door, which is okay. I haven't spoken to most of my shitface neighbours in years. Why? Because they're all white supremacist bigots! Lady called out to me this morning, after I was on the news. She leant over the fence. 'Pleee-ase, Marmeeee! Don't murder meee!' But my daughter was killed by a drunk and my son raped on a St Louis wharf, so I don't care."

Floyd

"The road to Emmaus, ladies and gentlemen, is a very boring walk. Luke said it was seven miles from Jerusalem, about which there is some scholarly dispute. What he didn't say is how boring those seven miles are. A stranger comes along and alleviates the boredom by engaging Cleopas and friend in conversation. Nobody would think there's anything very unusual in that. They get to talking about the death of the Galilean preacher and the stranger asks them who this preacher was. Well, Cleopas must have thought his new friend had crawled out from under a stone. Jesus was the *talk of the town*: everybody knew about this man and how his death had been signalled with strange meteorological events. But did Jesus reveal himself to them? No. I guess he used what we could call the Socratic method: he asked a question, ladies and gentlemen, because sometimes the lord Jesus, the risen lord, has to probe. No lights out of a sky. And the two travellers were downcast. They stopped in the middle of the road and looked very sad. Like they'd lost their one hope."

Curtis

"I'm a Leo. So you're skinny now and you walk and bike, but it's a losing battle, man, and come 40 you're gonna be an old man. Like I'm saying, all you need is four hours a week. You can carve four hours a week out of your schedule, and when you're 70 you could be like you're 40 and people will go: wow, *I* wanna chest and abs like that guy. And you're desirable, man, cause bottom line is – you're fat and 250lbs and who wants you? It's miserable. Twenty years' time, everyone's gonna be doing weights. We haven't begun to see the tip of the – and y'know, it isn't just a physical thing, it's mental. You work out, you release all those endomorphins, you're fired up and your mental capacity is greatly enhanced. You sleep better, I'm a light sleeper, but you dream better and you wake up feeling great, like let's *go*, instead of opening your eyes and thinking, uh-oh, gravity. You may think you're alert now, but just start doing weights and watch your horizons expand. I haven't done weights for four months but I've still got a great body, see? All you need is some pumpin' and musculature and people will be all over you, man. You stand up like this, instead of all hunched over, like this. That's what I tell Darryl but he doesn't listen."

Evelyn

"I've been a member of the League of Women Voters, who were, well, mostly suffragettes and educationalists, for many, many years. Since I was in college in the 1940s. And I belong to the Unitarian Church. I remember the race riots and segregation very well. We fought to keep a school open that white parents had boycotted because of colored admissions. And in '62, our church was bombed for supporting educational integration and the ministers threatened. My husband was set up by a local racist who rang pretending to be the husband of one of my teaching colleagues, and he expressed concern about me. Which was a threat. I got a note through the door late one night that said, 'What would you do if you had five minutes left to live?' Mike and I used to drive the kids to school who couldn't get here on segregated buses. Y'know, and people were murdered for less. That was what it was like, and everything continues. These streetcars were the same then as they are now. They still use sand to brake the cars and the St Charles depot has to cannibalize other vehicles across the country for the right parts. There's a city preservation order on them. Mike used to read aloud 'The Adventures of Isobel', do you know that poem? 'Isobel, Isobel, didn't worry, / Isobel didn't scream or scurry. / She washed her hands and she straightened her hair up. / Then Isobel quietly ate the bear up.' I love that poem."

Darryl

"I had an experience when I was I guess seven – eight? – that I've never forgotten. I heard Psalm 23 for the first time and I could not get the last line out of my head, 'And I will dwell in the House of the Lord for ever'. Not for forty days or forty nights, not for a thousand years, but for *ever*. That was it. It did something to me. I went to bed terrified: it was like I'd been injected. I was going to be imprisoned, and this was a good thing? It was the idea of being inside a house for ever. First dream, I saw my sister at the end of my bed with a big net on the end of a pole. I said, 'Linda.' She smiled back at me and that was the end of that. Then, second time, I heard this man's voice saying, 'In a moment you will be introduced to someone,' and I held my breath. Same voice said, 'You know who he is, don't you? I'm going to introduce you to the Devil. He's just coming,' and I waited some more. Then right inside my head, closer than ever, the deepest, realest voice said, 'Hello, Darryl,' and he knew my name and I woke up."

Evelyn

"We took some stuffed-shrimp po-boys and went out to LaBranche and paddled deep into the reserve. The fireflies were on and off like landing lights and tracer fire and I love it there but I was still on the look out for two pink eyes, close-set. They're hard to come by, but if you do, the best thing is to paddle past as swiftly and as silently as possible. I was doused in insect repellent because I react badly. Allergies build up. You have like a tank of resistance and when it gets full, you start to react. Anyway, I'm covered and Mike isn't because the bugs haven't begun to breed in earnest yet. It's only March. We take a turning into a deep swamp, out of an ox-bow lake, and eat one of the po-boys by one of Mike's landmark trees. Bullfrogs, crickets and toads. And then a marsh-frog puffing out its throat in the middle of a cypress shoot. Mike takes us further into a low thicket overhung with creeper and Spanish moss. I was quiet as could be but Mike was quieter, his paddle slipping in and out of the water without making a sound. I was holding the bicycle searchlight but the marsh-gas has its own luminosity. Then Mike slaps himself, some giant bug, and I reach forward and he tips the canoe right over and all of a sudden we're in the water and *we are prey*."

Lester

"What did I want in New York? I got tired of being able to touch everything everywhere I went, like *this*. What I paid for a one-bedroom apartment I pay here for a three-bedroom house with a two-car garage and a big garden. But that took time. When I first got here, man, I could *only* get arrested, you understand me? I came to Tulsa, why. Well, I had a girlfriend who moved back here and when I showed up and rang her from the station she almost fainted on the line, so that was a big mistake on my part right there. I was here and I was lost, no money, tired. I remember I caught a bus out to South Lewis 51st. On the map there was a Comfort Inn on 47th and Yale, except there was no through route to Yale and I had to trudge along the 51st Interstate. And it was much further than I'd anticipated. Mistake No 2: I approached a woman for directions and she ran for her car, got inside, secured the windows and waved me away. Like this, go away, go away, go away big black man. I was mouthing, 'All I want to do is ask you a question.' And she was, 'Go away, I don't want to know.' But that's the thing, there. You have a house, you have direction. You have a place to go. Motion towards. You have nowhere to go, conversation is aimless."

Wendy

"Now is really not a great time to visit Oklahoma City. Everyone's kinda moving about in a daze and we're all so distraught. I'm sorry. I know where the NW39th Express-way is, at least I've driven on it. Somewhere nearby? No, I don't have that information . . . oh, a hotel. Now wait a minute. This is so dumb, I can't seem to find . . . The West-side Y. Well, I know that's over on Martin Luther King. You can try them, sure, but it's in a black part of town. I don't know if that matters to you. You – you don't have a car? You're on foot? Without a car?"

John-Gerald

"The last time I took the bus I was sat next to this Mexican guy down from Missouri, with a home-cured pheasant. And he was waving this bird around, saying, 'See! See! It's not alive!' Right about after that I stopped my wandering. I'm not saying it was, you know, related. I'm not a racialist. This is a freedom we got here, supposedly. Even with all that you read and see and hear. But I got this sore chest. I got swollen glands and a bad head, and I'm not going to a doctor. I don't believe in them. There's only one doctor I believe in and if he's not gonna cure me, nothing will. He stopped my drinking, helped me quit cussing and beating up on my wife. I expect a miracle. Absolutely. Yes I do."

Kevin

"Josephus speaks of an Emmaus about four miles from Jerusalem. It was chosen by the Roman Emperor Vespasian as the site for a colony of soldiers in AD 70. But it's also identified with the modern Qaloniyeh because that name seems to be a corruption of the Latin *colonia*. And in Maccabean times, Amwas, which is fifteen miles from Jerusalem on the Jaffa Road, was known as Emmaus. Before it became Nicopolis. That's chapter and verse on Emmaus. You're welcome. Well, I had a good education. Oral Roberts University was very rigorous and well equipped. In 1977, it had an online database from which students could access any class. How many other institutions had that kind of facility?"

Kevin

"I don't think it's funny, no. And I don't think it's polite to invite someone into your house so that you can ridicule their beliefs. Cheap shots don't make your opponents cheap, you know. The Church of the, what, Revolving Door? But it doesn't even make sense. Oh, I get it. Okay. Open. Very clever. Look, I'm not here to deny the challenges, okay. I readily concede – I – yes, for those of us who grew up in conservative homes, it's difficult at best. I have to be a good Catholic to someone who's Hispanic and dying from AIDS, I have to able to minister to his family, if they're around. Or they may be Pentecostal, whatever. We are struggling against doctrine in so many ways. But against the far Right the unspoken truth is that we are winning. They want to attack us for our lifestyles but it's a difficult stance to maintain. And they can't dismiss us as an irrelevant cult or anomaly because we're bigger than 99% of all churches in America. And do they *not* want lesbians and gay men to go to church?"

Ruth

" 'A very gracious Texan woman, a prominent club member' – they don't say what club, I notice – 'stopped in for a drink at a soda fountain accompanied by her small daughter. She ordered Dr Pepper for both. "Because," she said to a friend at the same table, "I have seen the factory, the water, the fruit juices and the same kind of sugar I have on my table and I know it is healthful for my child".' I think it's kind of a shame that all the ads mention fruit juices but Dr Pepper doesn't actually have any. Maybe it did back then, I don't know. The water part is quite true, though. Waco has a number of artesian wells. And one 'crazy' well, so called because it is supposed to have cured a woman of her insanity. But the story I like best is the one about Lyndon B. Johnson, who had a vice-presidential edition of 100 bottles specially made, and they were supposed to be used for the first time during a visit by President and Mrs John F. Kennedy, scheduled for the evening of November 22, 1963. Oh, look. 'If Atlas were on earth, he would recommend Dr Pepper. It is liquid sunshine.' "

Thomas

"Do you know where I can get a steak and some eggs? Where there's a grill? Are you not from around here? I'm hungry. Yes sir. That would be appreciated. You not from around here? I just got discharged from the Fort Sam Medical Center. I have had various bits of me taken out over the past five years. To stop the cancer. To arrest the spread of it, and now I'm hungry, spite of the fact I have only half a stomach. And one lung. I have one lung. 165 stitches right across my abdomen. The cancer took a hold during my poker playing years. I was on four packets a day and two quarts of whisky. That's enough to embalm you."

Benita

"This was our schoolroom from first to sixth grade. As you can see it's half-demolished, those window frames had pretty paper blinds to keep the sun out. Look at it all! All crumbling and those foundations. Like bad teeth. I can't hardly bear to look at it myself, but I'm drawn. Every time I come back. My cousin took me in when my ma died. Pa died before I knew who he was, when I was a baby. I come back to see proud Lillie. She says there's some graffiti somewhere about with her name on it but I've never seen it. The descendants of the Indians still live nearby in conditions of direst poverty. Other of the missions you got wrecks of cars, here you're lucky if you find a tire and a plate. Find all kinds of things, lumps of fur look like roadkill that get up and walk! Either that or there's a mean dog waiting for you behind a fence it can jump. I was lucky. My cousins loved me. I know that for a fact, and that's not always true if you're mestizo in a Hispanic-white family, and you're brought up the only one who is because of some unspecified encounter no one really wants to go into anymore. You're either above or below the rest of the family always. It happens though and I'm the proof of that. I got a good education and I went to law school and I live well."

Harvey

"I'm an ex-Jew Catholic convert and my wife Kris is from Uruguay. She's not too happy about my shift in orthodoxies and I'm none too clear about it myself. I can see some kind of logical fallacy, certainly. If the commandment says 'honour thy father and thy mother', then I guess that means I should have stayed Jewish. At least I waited until my father was dead before converting. I'm a geologist for the government and I'm researching a nuclear facility near Los Alamos. It's amazing how you can do this technical thing and still have these ideological disputes with colleagues who are highly respected geologists in their own right but creationists at the same time. I am in an awful way with one guy, whom I like very much as a person. But he is obsessed with explaining away everything as a biblical relic. So, all the limestones from here to the canyon are carbonates that were reworked by the Flood, okay. He has nothing to say about the classic reefs that show up here. He is in total denial that New Mexico had any kind of coastal environment. It's crazy. And the dinosaur tracks in the Mesozoic rocks? How can they be late in the Flood like he says? I thought everything outside the Ark was supposed to be dead. Being a Jew Catholic sometimes feels like the least of my problems."

Blake

"The Cross of the Martyrs is a peculiar memorial. It's supposed to commemorate the Franciscans who were killed in the pueblo revolt of 1682, though no one feels that sorry about them now. I mean, it doesn't – well yes, it's awful, but is it really that unreasonable to suggest the Church had it coming? And the plaques on the way up. One is for a pastor who was kidnapped and killed in 1892, and another celebrates New Mexico's native heritage. I don't know. I think I like the graffiti on the picnic tables better. 'Amerikka – Land of the Nobody'. 'Take A Stand – Rich People Are Running Our State'. And how about this one, I like this: 'D.A.R.E – Drugs Are Really Excellent.' Someone's added, 'I know'."

Deann

"Body Electronics is a holistic protocol with meditative technologies and nutritional programs. There's a seminar I attend every Thursday evening. Geoff's an inspirational teacher. Everyone loves Geoff. He's one of only two BE teachers in the States. We start with the anointment, which is where you rub non-alcohol based peppermint extract on your temples to facilitate concentration and ward off negative thought patterns. Then we get into the discussion, which is another means of transcendence. So the great thing about BE is that you don't just realize the beauty of each instant, you actually get to live for ever. We have four bodies: physical, mental, emotional and spiritual. And death is a state of mind that the rejuvenative mental body can overcome. Here's hoping! I – I do think I have a different perspective to the other members of the group, yes. Well, I have a different set of expectations you might say. It's just the niceness and the calm I value. I mean, I have objections to the immortal part of it because I don't see what it can do about sudden death – plane crashes and earthquakes and wars. I don't see how I can rejuvenate if I'm in a hundred bits and pieces. And if we're immortal why are we all different ages? But I don't want to pick holes. It's the feeling of being in a group of nice people. I feel safe. And feeling safe and calm is a great analgesic by the way. My parents are on the East Coast, Westchester. It's hard for them. And I get everywhere on my own and for as long as I have left I choose this. This is my car. It was nice meeting you."

Tanis

"We're 7,500 feet above sea level and I call this the land of Plenty. Valley is really the wrong word as you can see. What we're looking at is a pastoral plain torn in two by the Rio Grande gorge. We're over on Ranchitos Lane. I'm native and I've known my neighbours all my life. I went to college in California, came back and met Blake in the Peace Corps. Now we're part-time school-workers. I'm a careers counsellor for teenagers in remote rural communities and Blake works with the educationally disadvantaged and emotionally, uh, distorted on outward-bound projects. We have our own wood-burning stove. And lots and lots of axes."

Kris

"I punish the saint. It is like a punishment until the thing happens. You can pray to the idol for health, harvests, prosperity in the normal way, but if misfortune occurs we go like this, and this, and *this*. The saints are walled up by mothers if their sons are missing or get kidnapped by Indians. When I was little I knew a shepherd-boy who disappeared for nearly a year and his mother had a wooden saint for the safety of her son. She buries the effigy. One day she hears knocking behind the plaster and her saint falls out of his place in the wall. The next day her son returns home. I like this punishing. It goes back a long, long way. I descend from the Penitentes, originally. We no longer beat ourselves with sticks – but still we have visions. God is everywhere. Our Lady of Guadalupe, the local shrine, remembers the woman who saw Christ in a tortilla. And the church was moved. A farmer found a saint in his backyard. He took it to his church and gave it to the priest. In his field the next day he sees the same image staring up at him from the dirt. Eventually – this goes on for many weeks – they move the church to his fields because it is a sign the building belongs there instead."

Rosamund

"I do miss home terribly, particularly Annette. We were very close. But on the other hand I'm still vastly enthusiastic about everything I love here, particularly my work – experimental psychology, they may call it something else now, I don't know – and the value of the *culture* and the land itself, of course. That enormous long strip of water boiling away at the bottom. Isn't it extraordinary? It never ceases to amaze me. But out here is what we call the valley proper, you see. Yes! We did it all ourselves. And look at the ceiling, and the walls. Genuine adobe. Feet thick. Well, the Spanish are pretty useless at everything, really, but they have managed to keep their religion pure, and that's what I like."

Evelyn

"My ex-husband lived on floor eleven when we met. I was on floor twelve, but there was a public phone on the floor below. In fact it was in the elevator that I met Mike. I'm sure it was an elevator because when I got in I was on floor eleven and when we got out we were in the car lot. There seems no other reasonable explanation. And we were married and had sweet Jessie a year later."

Ed

"Or what? Revolutionary mystics in the Middle Ages thought all Jews were child-killers. Demons, Herodian Demons. If you're really surprised when I say to you the abortion issue and anti-Semitism are inextricably linked, if you're convinced it's a slander, then read some fucking history. But you've taken a leap of faith, I can see that. That's the trouble. 'I'm not the one who needs to feel shame.' Yes, you are. We do, everyone. You're so confident that all that can be said about God has been said already that you don't open a book apart from the one you're least equipped to read. Look, really look, at the people doing the accusing. Look at where they come from, who they admire. You've made a choice. You're so sure. So unnaturally sure. You know they've done tests on depressed people, people like me who are depressed by people like you, and you know what they found? People who are depressed are the realists. We give a speech, write an article, we know we're fucking losers and half the audience is bored and the other half are pissed off in some private, resentful way, think they can do better. You get up, full of fucking can-do and clap your hands while your pastor fucks little black boys and you say fuck Islam, fuck everyone, fuck the gays, fuck the free press, fuck it all just give me my fucking donuts and insurance. And I'm the baby-betraying coward. Because I don't shoot doctors. You're fucking *insane*."

Darryl

"Some people overstate everything, but you can get a long way by sounding as if you know what you're talking about. Me, I just think life is precious and that we shouldn't seek to curtail it, and that art and shared interests and laughter and the imagination can sustain it. And the truth, certainly. But not held on to, not kinda grabbed, do you know what I mean? I think the balance of probability is – if the deer on the plain hears a rustle, it knows. The instinct is trained. Of course the rustle may be a rabbit not a lion, but the deer has no pride. It can take being wrong, and so can I. I'm wrong about just about everything."

MAX EGREMONT

Anniversary

In the restaurant, she wondered how many times Will might refer to the number forty. It was her fortieth birthday: that was why they were here. He was in the habit of repeating himself, like the just too loud tick of an old clock – similar to those that he admired when they were searching for furniture for the new house.

'I can date this one,' he had said in an antique shop. 'Remember that old man in Burford who wouldn't come down in price? It's the same – but forty per cent less. The Victorians knew about solidity.' Not only the Victorians, she thought. But he could shake, with laughter or anger. You just needed to touch him in the right place.

Will was a numbers man whereas it was words that interested her, especially the names of places that she associated with beauty or danger, preferably both. She'd even been to some of them but now she depended on news reports or her memory: Kandahar, Peshawar, the Rann of Kutch, Samarkand, Tblisi.

In the run-up to the birthday, she had wondered what he would do and had stayed silent about it, not so much to see if he remembered – his memory was good – but how long he needed to think of a suitable fortieth evening.

Forty. It was a number that Will looked upon with scorn and he'd refused to buy the forty per cent less clock. 'Never settle for forty,' he said at another time, speaking of a prospective deal. 'Fifty per cent at least to start with and then build on it.' Fifty was good, a bold step, whereas forty meant smallness, inadequacy. After Jane had been born, he'd said, with noticeable triumph, 'We'll need fifty per cent more space – not now but when she's older. That's what we've got to work towards.'

Older? Now she thought of how their daughter Jane might be at forty – and herself at seventy. What would there be to build on at seventy? Will would be with her all the time, not leaving early each weekday (and sometimes week-end) morning for the tube, the figure fifty having been passed and built on: forty a mere memory of an evening out.

Eventually he came up with the plan, his hand clasping hers one night across the kitchen table, his ring over her ring, each golden bright. It came quickly, like the rush with which he spoke sometimes of his bonus prospects – as if the figures might vaporize into the air. His mother would look after Jane – he had fixed that – and they would go north but only if she liked the plan: first to Luton airport: then he named the foreign city.

'Won't it be very cold?' she asked.

He had to admit that it would be cold – very, very cold – but romantic with the sun on the snow and the baroque palaces, the place empty. The package was for a long week-end, the hotel, the flight. Could she get the clinic to let her go for the Monday and the Friday, could those who needed the therapy that she gave be shifted to other days? 'You'll need to approach them now. Give plenty of warning.' He mentioned a figure. 'It's about forty per cent of your week.'

When Will had been forty, he'd wanted nothing and had worked late, as if to show his contempt for the number: agreeing reluctantly to meet her at a restaurant, smiling politely when she spoke of the babysitter with whom they had left Jane: a crop-haired tattooed girl, the same one they'd had a month earlier, who was interested in the stars and the shape of numbers. The babysitter, told of the reason for the night out, had spoken of the phallic lift of the two strokes that rise from the crossbar of the figure four.

'Really?' Will had said when she reported the girl's words. 'But the smaller one goes down as well as up from the cross-stroke. What does she read into that?'

Probably a life descending as well as rising: both possi-ble. It could go either way. 'Shall we ask her when we get back?'

'I'd rather not.'

The northern city *was* cold. But Will was right; the sun

lifted the place: the gabled roofs, the pale and golden palaces, the cobbled squares, even the Soviet-era buildings on the way in from the airport. He'd planned the trip entirely by himself, making her promise not even to look the place up on the web, wanting, she thought, her pleasure to join his delight in his ingenuity, raising them both from the crossbar. She hoped that he hadn't packed too much in, that she would have time. Always Will was in a hurry, anxious to get on – and so there might be no let up, from the big dinner on the first night which was the birthday. She would let him do what he wanted, making room for both of them, for his rush and for her steadiness, the healing part of her.

'Take care, please,' the man behind the desk in the hotel said as they went out to the restaurant. 'The ice . . .' His English, almost accentless, faded on the last word, leaving a smile. 'It is an occasion, I think?'

She looked at Will, who pressed her arm and said, 'I told him. That's why there were flowers in the room.'

She thought again of what the tattooed girl had said: the phallic strokes up but also the long cross-stroke of the four: flat, flaccid, finished – but with at least an idea that it might stretch on. It could go either way; things were not settled. 'How many other people here know?' she said and reached across to kiss him. They were the same height, level in the street where a path had been made through the piled-up dirty snow, icy, lethal if they fell.

'Look up,' Will said. Hardly daring to take her eyes away from the ice, she pushed the warm, heavy hat he had given her higher on her forehead so that she could see the stars, some clustered in speckled groups that the tattooed girl could have named. 'A real winter sky,' he said and, not looking at her, put a gloved hand on her shoulder, pulling her to him: then pressed his face into her cheek, whispering, 'Forty'; soft, quite deep, the last syllable prolonged: then in his normal voice, still quiet, the words heavy with feeling, 'I never thought I'd be so lucky. At university, when I saw you, I never thought . . . And then Jane, all part of our perfect world.' Then his feet, or one of them, slid away, tipping his body deeper into her and she held him, keeping them both upright. 'Whoops!'

How far is this restaurant? she wondered. Will was saying something else, still holding her as they edged slowly forward. 'In the outlying areas here, the temperature can get down to . . .' He paused. Was a joke coming? Sometimes he took time to set these up, as if clearing a site. 'Forty below zero!' She thought of the descending line. '*Really* freezing.'

Only about five – or four – minutes further. He guided her slowly into a twisting side street, towards a light above a heavy closed wooden door that opened to reveal a large dark-suited man who, as they entered, said, 'Is it permitted to wish a happy birthday?' – before leading them into a large panelled full room where voices shouted against music of bouncing wildness or sobbing despair.

They were put in a cubicle, beside each other on a banquette yet apart from everyone, raised up, linked to the rest of the room only by a small step, as if held. A bottle of champagne in an ice bucket on a small table in front of them, resembled, she thought, a boulder blocking the way out of a cave.

The noise. How loud it was, how quickly any break in the roaring voices was filled by the music's extreme emotion, the panelling apparently absorbing nothing. They shrieked their orders to the dark-suited man who bent very close to them. 'Weekend parties,' he said. 'Some from England!'

She stared at one group seated at a round table in the centre of the room. At first they made her think again of the tattooed girl but then she saw that these, although young, were not vague or dreamy or vegetarian but drunk: perhaps what her father and some of her patients at the clinic might call 'yobs'. What were they saying? There were eight of them, four of each sex. As she strained to hear their words, Will, next to her on the banquette, ran through the city's recent history – history was another of his things – his words indistinct although she caught the dates: '1940, 1946, 1989', years of pain or hope: then there was a yell from the round table and the music, briefly, stopped.

'I can't fucking well see time, can I?' one man shouted. 'Look!' He held up a long glass, half full. 'Not like this!' He drank from it and, as if in timed acclaim, a chord crashed out from the sound system.

She settled back, against the flow of Will's words, their story also invisible yet soothing, a deep flow, time on its way – just the dates clear, posts on a path. Now he'd reached the end of the communist era and opportunities for investment.

This was the sound not only of the past but of her life with him, solid with fact, the cubicle around them, champagne in front: the smooth progression of dishes offered up like easy chances. She thought – tonight, the noise, the rich food, the wine, the history, the sex: tomorrow, the sex, the history, the wine, the rich food, the noise and the sex again: then the flight home and the move on from forty.

This was her land but one could look across the frontier. Two of the round-table party were the leaders, she thought – a boy and a girl: thin, eager and they seemed beautiful. The girl was shouting, 'Why not fucking go there? See where they went on that last trek – the real route.' Then a list of names: 'Peshawar, Nuristan, Drosh, Chitral, Vakhan, the Wakhan Corridor': danger and freedom, each greeted with a cheer and raised glasses. 'You can only get fucking killed!'

Will had reached the country's awesome reserves of shale gas. 'Potentially transformational but the present government is facing a fascinating dilemma – concern for the environment against not only energy independence but the export option as well.' He stopped suddenly and she noticed a flurry to their left. The dark-suited man had arrived with another man in a chef's hat carrying a smallish round white iced cake with one burning candle erect on its glazed surface. She jumped. 'No singing of "Happy Birthday", I promise!' Will said, laughing. 'No shouting of forty! But I couldn't resist.'

Before she kissed him, she looked across the cake – another stone across the exit – and thought that no one else had noticed. But then the girl who had called out those names glanced at her, taking in the fortieth scene – not with scorn or amusement but just as an interval before returning to her glass.

STUART EVERS

Charter Year, 1972

She had been told, tucked up, kissed goodbye: expected to rest. He had given her earplugs, placed them in the palm of her hand. Sleep, he'd said. You need it. Sleep. They were on the bedside table now, sticky-ended with wax, slightly crushed. Her heart was audible when she wore them, an uncomfortable sound, so she'd taken them out just as soon as he'd inched the bedroom door shut.

Yvette's eyes were closed, but only to concentrate on the sound of wheels scraping the hallway floor, his duffel coat being taken from a hat rack, the controlled rattle of the door chain. She opened them when the front door was quietly closed and, in her nightdress, hurried through the hallway and made for the lounge window.

She leant against the sill and looked up the road, him and the pram under the blushes of lamppost light. The road was steep, winding; bungalows neatly spaced along it. She missed stairs. She missed height. And now she missed David, and her child.

Their leaving made her too anxious to move from the window. While, outside, David tried to soothe Dylan, tried to stop his constant scream, she stayed by the window, waiting. She would not sleep; but, on their return, would pretend she had. It was, by now, an accomplished act: a stretching yawn, a quarter roll to the other side of the bed, an unnecessary, 'What time is it?'

There were pills in the house. Bottles of them, brown like beer. The doctor urged her to take them. Sometimes she weighed them in her hands, but always put them back under the cotton wool. There were natural remedies too; herbal tonics and St John's wort. These she had taken in quantity, but their effectiveness was minimal. It wasn't something she liked to admit. She told David that she was fine. Just tired.

He would come home from work in the car and busy himself with their son. He'd kiss her and ask her seriously about her day. She'd talk about Dylan: his bowel movements, his sleep patterns, his brief moments of quiet. And David would say: But what about you? How have you been? At this she'd seethe, make claws of hands. His understanding, his kindness, his patience! And she would say: Fine. I'm fine, my love. David's smile would be perfect, and told her flatly of her own, singular failures.

*

There was a car parked outside their bungalow. David saw it from the top of the hill, Dylan finally asleep in the pram.

Its interior light was on, the engine idling. David was careful to keep a steady speed on the way down, avoiding ruts in the pavement, the occasional patches of ice. When he reached the third lamppost, he recognized the car. It was a Jaguar, an older model: racing green, creamy leather seats. He pushed the pram past it and the door opened.

'Mr Coville?' The man smiled. 'I saw you on Moody Street. You passed my house. I would have called but I don't have your telephone number.'

'We don't have a phone, Mr Stevens,' David said.

'No. Of course not. How silly of me. May I come inside? I need to talk to you about a few things.'

'We were just going to get the little one off to bed, Mr Stevens.'

'It won't take a moment,' he said, getting out of the car and putting on a hat. 'Won't take any time at all.'

Stevens was tall, taller with his hat. He picked up an attaché case from the passenger seat. David looked down at Dylan and waved Stevens towards the house.

'That's a beauty,' Stevens said pointing at the car on the driveway. 'French, is it?'

'Swedish,' David said. 'A Volvo.'

'I only buy British myself,' Stevens said. 'You always know where you are with a Jaguar.' David nodded and opened the door. Yvette would pretend to be asleep. He wondered how long she would keep up the pretence. Long enough, he hoped, for Stevens to be long gone.

*

Dylan was born to the sound of fireworks and firecrackers, a few moments after the turn of 1972 – the seven-hundredth anniversary of the town's charter being granted. There had been complications. A caesarean section was required. It would have been a natural birth, home-conducted and drug-free. But, instead, David had stood in a waiting room, drinking coffee, making small talk with a man from the town. It was the man's fourth and he had not been present at any of the births. He was red-faced and swaying drunk. Without Yvette's complications, David would have been there when Dylan was born, and this man's daughter would have been the baby on the front page of the local newspaper, under the headline: 'Charter Baby Arrives Right on Time'.

*

'I've been to India,' Stevens said. 'During the war it was. Hot. Damned hot.' He was standing next to the crammed bookshelves, holding one of the small Vishnus. Most of them had been bought at a head shop in Liverpool.

'Yvette and I went after university. We stayed on an ashram. It was quite something.'

'Is that right? There's an Indian family in town now, you know that? Moved here from Stockport. They're opening a restaurant, so I hear.'

His accent was neutral; unlike any David had heard in the town. Stevens opened his attaché case. It was filled with papers, his handwriting all over them.

'Sorry, Mr Stevens—'

'Robert, please.'

'Sorry, Robert, but Yvette is sleeping and I have to get the dinner on . . .'

'I completely understand. New family, new pressures, what? I just want to run through some things with you.' He passed over a carbon-copied sheet of paper. Names and dates. Time and schedules.

'This is of course only a provisional list of engagements, but I think all the major ones are covered. It's nothing too arduous. Just turn up, pose for a few photographs, then a meet and greet, as I like to call it. Shouldn't take more than an hour or so.'

Stevens smiled as David looked down the list, the type smudgy and the paper thin. There was at least one event every month, with several clustered around July and August. David rolled a cigarette as he read down the list once, then twice. He lit the cigarette and shook his head.

'I'm sorry, Mr Stevens, this just won't be possible. We might be able to do some of these, but we have commitments and people to visit. And that's without even thinking about the strain on Yvette and Dylan.' Stevens took the spectacles from his nose and wiped them on a spotted handkerchief.

'I do understand,' Stevens said. 'But there isn't much I can do. I said at the time, believe me I said to the committee when they were programming this, that it was one heck of a schedule. But there isn't anything we can do. It is what it is. And I did explain when we gave you your prizes that you'd be expected to join in the festivities.'

'You didn't say it would be a year-long commitment, though.'

Stevens hitched up his trousers. 'The town takes Charter Year very seriously. We've been planning this for five years, if you can believe it. It might be difficult to understand for those new to the area, but this is the most important year in the town's history. The Queen is coming to visit. *It's a Knockout* is being filmed here. It's a chance to really put us on the map.'

The bluff of smoke obscured the flash of David's smile. He had met Yvette on a CND rally. They had demonstrated on countless protests, joined underground political parties, smoked opium with poets. They were living in a bungalow, loaning out their baby for Tories to kiss and a monarch to hold.

'We can't do it,' David said. 'I'm sorry.'

Stevens stood and went to the window. He twitched the curtains.

'It is a nice motor, isn't it? Must be practical too, what with having a new child. I notice you drive it to work too. I see you as you pass of a morning on the way to Batemans. Mr Bateman is a good boss, isn't he? He's a good friend of mine too, is Ken. A good friend of the town. His family's been here nine generations, I believe.'

David laughed. 'What are you trying to say, Stevens?'

'Simply that there are legal considerations – the car was a prize contingent on your being involved in Charter Year. And there are other things to take into account, too. Your standing in the town is very important. Not as important as your livelihood, but still . . .'

Stevens had left the curtains open. The Volvo had mud around the back tyre, but the rest of the bodywork was clean and gleaming.

'You can't take the car.' It came out so quickly, so forcefully, it surprised David.

Stevens rubbed his hand over his chin. 'Farmer's was very kind to donate it as a prize. They want you turning up to all the functions in it. You must understand the predicament?'

David put out his cigarette and stood.

'This is ridiculous. We didn't even enter the prize. You just turned up with a photographer and that was that.'

'No one thought for a minute that you wouldn't be honoured, you see, Mr Coville. Jack Jervis was most disappointed to miss out. And to someone who's only been here five minutes too. In the circumstances, it really ought to be him who has the benefit of the car. Especially as there was some controversy—'

'What do you mean, controversy? Because Yvette had to have a caesarean? Are you serious?'

'All I am saying, Mr Coville, is that there are options. Other people who would be more than willing to take your place. We don't want to do that, but it is an option. Just work with us, Mr Coville. Please.'

The door opened. Yvette was dressed in slacks and a blue blouse, her hair tied loosely back. Mr Stevens half-rose from the sofa. Yvette ignored him, bent down to kiss her baby, then kissed David on the cheek. She gave her hand to Mr Stevens and offered tea. Stevens declined.

'I couldn't help but overhear, Mr Stevens. Would you mind if I saw the schedule?' she said.

Stevens passed it to her. She held it in one hand, the other circled around David's waist.

'David is very protective of me,' she said. 'I've not been well since the birth. But I'm better now. And this all seems fine to me. I know we've not been in town for very long, but we love it here. The people are so friendly. And I promise we'll do everything we can in this very special year for the town.'

She squeezed David just below the ribs. Mr Stevens smiled, exposing his stained teeth and greying tongue.

'Are you sure, Mrs Coville? I don't wish to pressure you.'

'No pressure necessary. It would be an honour. But we do need to get on. I'm sure you understand.'

He stood, thanked them for their time and understanding, then peered down into the pram.

'Beautiful little thing, isn't he?'

'We think so,' Yvette said. 'I'm sure the town will too.'

Stevens picked up his hat and retrieved his coat. From the car, he waved with gloved hands and sped away.

'Honey—'

'Shhh,' Yvette said. 'Don't worry, love. It's all OK.'

They embraced until Dylan began to scream. He screamed as Yvette picked him up, screamed as she kissed him, screamed as she tried to calm him down.

Charter Year, 1972

'We're going to have some fun, you and me,' she whispered to him as he screamed. 'It'll be a year no one forgets.'

Dylan screamed as she put him down. He screamed as she sang him a lullaby. He screamed for a long, long time.

ELLEN FELDMAN

Picador's 40th

In the world of numbers, 40 lacks panache. It does not have the heady breaking-into-the-double-digit excitement of 10, the impressive achievement of 50, the monumental stature of 100. It doesn't even have the artistic elegance of 3 or the superstitious looniness of 13. But for me, an American writer who has happily published three books with Picador, all of them set in the mid-twentieth century, 40 has enormous resonance—if you put the number 19 before it.

1940 was a crucial year, perhaps even a turning point, in what we have come to regard as the special relationship between the United Kingdom and the United States. At the time, life in the two countries was starkly, and from the British point of view heartbreakingly, different.

England had been at war, albeit a "phony war," for four months. In January, rationing began. By June, all of western Europe had fallen, and 340,000 men of the British Expeditionary Force were evacuating Dunkirk by just about every type of vessel imaginable, leaving an arsenal of equipment behind. England stood alone, its supply lifelines terrifyingly vulnerable.

On July 10, the German air force launched the Battle of Britain. For the next three and a half months, British fighter squadrons inflicted stunning damage in daily air battles against superior numbers, but the Germans continued to wreak havoc on essential shipping. In September, the Blitz began. In November, the German air force, though defeated in the Battle of Britain, continued to rain death on London with exhausting regularity, and extended its saturation bombing to Coventry and other British towns. Berlin spoke of Coventryizing the entire island.

Across the Atlantic, life was sunnier. Thanks in part to war production, America was climbing out of the depression. People had jobs and money in their pockets. Glossy magazines grew fat with ads for sleek new cars, stylish evening dresses, aged whisky, and other accoutrements of the good life. Broadway was aflame not with bombs but with neon signs advertising plays and movies, restaurants and nightclubs.

Americans were not unaware of the war or Britain's hardship. When the smoke-cured voice of Edward R. Murrow, intoning "This . . . is London," crackled over the airwaves, chills ran down America's collective spine. But if many Americans sympathized, few wanted to get involved. Neutrality was the official policy of the government; isolationism the creed of much of the population. Some German-Americans, Italian-Americans, Irish-Americans, and non-hyphenated Americans did not even sympathize. They believed aid to Great Britain was illegal, ill-considered, and futile. The most fervent of them united in an organization called America First, which boasted among its leaders Charles A. Lindbergh. The kidnapping and death of his small son had put the lie to the nickname Lucky Lindy, but he was still a towering all-American hero whose opinions carried weight. Lindbergh was not the only prominent American to oppose aid to Great Britain. Joseph P. Kennedy, the ambassador to England, believed Britain's struggle against Hitler was doomed. His son, John F. Kennedy, contributed to America First secretly.

But as 1940 progressed, President Roosevelt became more and more certain that the U.S. had to find a way to supply Great Britain. The problem was that America's "Cash and Carry" law stipulated that England had to pay for war supplies in dollars, and by 1940, Britain was on the verge of bankruptcy in terms of dollar credits. Always cagey by instinct—"I never let my left hand know what my right hand is doing"—FDR was, in this situation, duplicitous by necessity. He knew he could not get too far ahead of the American people. Nonetheless, he could not stop worrying the problem. "We must find some way to lease or even lend these goods to the British," he began saying to aides.

In November, FDR was elected to an unprecedented third term. Churchill, Great Britain, and American intervention-ists waited for him to take action. Instead, he boarded the

U.S.S. *Tuscaloosa* for a two-week fishing trip in Southern waters. The post-election presidential holiday is a longstanding and much deserved tradition, but not when the world is going up in flames.

From a sporting point of view, the trip was a bust. Even a radio message from Ernest Hemingway suggesting the First Fisherman try the Mona Passage between the Dominican Republic and Puerto Rico and use a feathered hook baited with a piece of pork rind yielded no strikes. But FDR, who was always happy on the water, continued to enjoy his holiday, and it was, to all appearances, a holiday. His only official duties consisted of inspecting island bases. At Guantanamo Bay, still a name without dark associations, he laid in a hefty supply of Cuban cigars, though he was a chain cigarette-smoker. At Jamaica, St. Lucia, and Antigua, he entertained British colonial officials and their wives. Off Eleuthera Island, he met with the Duke of Windsor and recommended a program similar to the Civilian Conservation Corps, which had put men to work during the Depression.

In the evening, he played poker or watched Hollywood movies. The crew's favorite was *Tin Pan Alley*, starring Betty Grable. We have no record of the President's opinion of it, but we do know policy discussions were notably absent. The only serious adviser aboard was Harry Hopkins. "I didn't know for a quite a while what he was thinking about, if anything," Hopkins wrote.

But FDR had not forgotten the war, or the four-thousand-word cable from Churchill, which had been delivered with other official mail by navy seaplane. In it, Churchill laid out the broad outlines and minute details of the military situation, assessed the critical problems of production, and emphasized the crucial importance of shipping in the Atlantic. When he turned to the financial outlook, he was brutally candid. "The moment approaches when we will no longer be able to pay cash for shipping and other supplies."

The question, as FDR saw it, was not if the US should send aid, but how to find a way around America's neutrality laws in order to send aid. While FDR sat in the sun, baited his hook, and cast his line, while he mixed his trademark terrible cocktails, regaled his guests with stories, and watched Betty Grable, he never stopped searching for a solution.

"But then," Hopkins went on, describing the fishing trip, "I began to get the idea that he was refueling, the way he so often does when he seems to be resting and carefree. So I didn't ask him any questions. Then, one evening, he suddenly came out with it—the whole program. He didn't seem to have any clear idea how it could be done legally. But there wasn't a doubt in his mind that he'd find a way to do it."

On December 16, rested, tanned, his usual ebullient self, FDR returned to Washington. The following day he held a press conference. FDR had revolutionized the American press conference. One could say he turned it into an art form. Before him, they were dreary affairs in which presidents offered ponderous replies to previously submitted written questions. Formality had been the keynote. Now FDR lounged behind his big memento-cluttered desk, his cigarette holder clamped between his shining teeth, his smile lighting up the room. The reporters crowded in, jostling for position and the chance to fire the first question. No matter how newsworthy his answers were going to be, the President always began by saying he had nothing of major importance to discuss that day. On December 17, 1940, he slid into the conference by the same sleight of hand, then segued into a brilliantly disingenuous riff.

"In my memory, and your memory, and in all history, no major war has ever been won or lost through lack of money . . . Now what I am trying to do is eliminate the dollar sign. That is something brand new in the thoughts of everybody in this room, I think—get rid of the silly, foolish, old dollar sign.

"Well, let me give you an illustration: Suppose my neighbor's home catches fire, and I have a length of garden hose four or five hundred feet away. If he can take my garden hose and connect it up with his hydrant, I may help him to put out his fire. Now, what do I do? I don't say to him before that operation, 'Neighbor, my garden hose cost me $15; you have to pay me $15 for it.'. . . What is the transaction that goes on? I don't want $15—I want my garden hose back after the fire is over."

Twelve days later, FDR went on the air with a Fireside Chat, another of his techniques for selling the American public complicated radical ideas with homey analogies, though the analogy he chose that evening as people gathered around their radios was not homey but stirring. "We must become the great arsenal of democracy," he told them. It was the birth of Lend Lease.

The bill did not pass without a struggle. Charles Lindbergh testified against it. Ambassador Kennedy's statements were so muddled that no one was sure where he stood. One senator predicted it would mean "ploughing under every fourth American boy." But it did pass Congress and had American support staunchly behind it.

"Thinking people are more and more coming to the view," the British ambassador, Lord Halifax, told London, "that the United States and the British Empire will have to stand very close and share responsibility for keeping peace in the world."

Much disharmony and discord lay ahead. The two nations spoke the same language but did not necessarily agree on the meaning of the words. American G.I.s were often miffed by English practices, traditions, weather, and the monetary system. British subjects complained that the Yanks were oversexed, overpaid, and over here. The sniping continued. To this day, the British see America as a Johnny-come-lately to the war. Americans have been known to congratulate themselves on saving England's hash. But these are the squabbles of siblings. The bonds that underlie the relationship go back a long way, but in the fortieth year of the twentieth century, the two nations took a giant step toward each other. As an American writer published by the fine not-so-old house of Picador, I am overjoyed to celebrate the friendship and the anniversary.

SUZETTE FIELD

Forty Parties in Forty Weeks

In 2011 Picador commissioned an idea I had pitched to them, to write a book to be called *A Curious Invitation* about famous parties in literature. My initial plan was to include thirty-five soirées, balls, fetes and bashes, featuring in works ranging from Plato's *Symposium* in Ancient Greece to Jackie Collins's *Hollywood Wives*. But after receiving suggestions for additional parties from various quarters I decided to expand the number to forty. This seemed like a nice round figure; without being too round, like fifty. It also resonated with classical significance: Lent lasts for forty days, it rained for forty days and forty nights in the Great Flood and Ali Baba faced forty thieves. Also it hadn't escaped my attention that 2012 would mark Picador's 40th anniversary and there's never anything wrong with a first-time author seeking to ingratiate themselves with their publisher.

Before very long life decided to hand me a second dead-line, which also involved the number forty. I became pregnant. In obstetrics the human gestation period is defined as 280 days, i.e. exactly forty weeks. To my alarm I realized that my two delivery dates, baby one (my book) and baby two (my baby), would coincide pretty much exactly. There were similarities between the two entities I was nurturing within me. Both would be a long haul, involving a certain amount of pleasure and a definite amount of suffering, but would supply an end product which would bring me pride and joy and, if I was lucky, might support me in my old age.

The literary task that lay ahead of me involved not only a lot of writing but a serious amount of reading. Forty prose works of various lengths had to be perused, including such heavyweights as Thackeray, Dostoyevsky and Proust. In a cowardly fashion I decided to start with the easy (and short) texts: Lewis Carroll, Gogol and Edgar Allan Poe. Poe's 'The Masque of the Red Death' comes in at a trim eight pages (not that this stopped Roger Corman making a full length horror movie of it), which compared favourably to *The Brothers Karamazov*, which weighs in at a hefty 760 pages.

In week twelve I was researching Daphne du Maurier (the Manderley Fancy Dress Ball in *Rebecca* is one of the parties I write about) and I learned that she, like me, was pregnant with her second daughter while writing the novel. In her case the baby was delivered before the book. More worryingly this daughter, Flavia, ended up writing a less than flattering biography of her mother, accusing her of putting her writing career before her children. I hoped that my unborn girl wouldn't harbour similar resentments against me in later life, telling the world that I had been too busy on my laptop to find time to expose her to Mozart symphonies in the womb.

At week sixteen I was writing about the Flying Party, a never-ending cocktail party hovering above an alien planet from Douglas Adams's *Life, the Universe and Everything*. Adams, I found, was famous for missing deadlines and on one occasion had only written a single sentence of his book when his due date arrived (he said he liked the 'whooshing sound' deadlines made when they flew past). With a dozen chapters under my belt, I reassured myself, at least I was doing better than him.

In week twenty it was Mrs Leo Hunter's Costume Breakfast in *The Pickwick Papers*. Pickwick, I discovered, came about largely by accident. The unknown twenty-four-year-old Dickens had been commissioned to provide the text for a monthly series of illustrations on sporting life by artist Robert Seymour. Unfortunately Seymour committed suicide after volume one, but this gave Dickens (who knew nothing about sport) the opportunity to repoint the serial in a more generally socially satirical direction. Within a year he was a celebrity. He of course went on to write a dozen more famous novels. This gave me a positive example of how a rookie author's career could unexpectedly blossom (not that I would wish anything unpleasant to befall my lovely and talented illustrator, Lynn Hatzius).

A fortnight later I was served up with a sobering counter-example to Dickens. *Cold Comfort Farm* was also Stella Gibbons's first novel (I cover Dick Hawk-Monitor's twenty-first-birthday party in my book) and catapulted her to fame in her early thirties. She went on to write thirty-one further books, pretty much none of which anyone has ever heard of, and never managed to repeat the runaway success of her first prose opus.

Sadder still was the story behind the novel I dealt with in week twenty-seven. *The Tale of Genji* was completed in Japan in the Heian period, some time in the early eleventh century, and contains a Blossom Viewing Party where the emperor and his courtiers inspect the newly arrived blossoms on the cherry tree in the gardens of the imperial palace. Not only does Genji have a strong case for being the world's first novel, but it was written by a woman. And it's still in print, in dozens of languages, a thousand years after its first appearance. The tragedy is that though the work has survived, we know almost nothing about its author, not even her real name (in Heian Japan it was disrespectful to refer to well-born people by their actual names, and the name attributed to her, Murasaki Shikibu, is an honorific title, the first name meaning 'purple' and the second deriving from the rank her father held at the imperial court).

A. A. Milne's Pooh Party (week thirty) offered me another aspirational role model. His two Pooh books, *Winnie-the-Pooh* and *The House at Pooh Corner*, have been translated into thirty-six languages, including Frisian, Mongolian,

Esperanto and Latin, and sold tens of millions of copies worldwide. Yet the two works total fewer than seventy thousand words between them, which must make Milne one of the biggest grossing authors of all time on a money-per-word basis. All the wealth and fame that Pooh brought him didn't stop Milne grumbling, as he surmised that his stories of soft toys would mean that his plays and detective novels (which he considered his proper works) would be utterly forgotten. And they were.

A couple of weeks later I treated myself to *The Three Musketeers*, which features the Paris City Aldermen's Ball, where d'Artagnan has to retrieve the Queen's lost diamonds to foil the machinations of the villainous Cardinal Richelieu. Here I came across the cautionary tale of Alexandre Dumas (père), who was not just a writer but a whole literary industry in his own right. Dumas employed a team of hack writers to churn out historical fiction under his brand and ended up with over a thousand published books to his name. Yet he still managed to spend the final years of his life in penury, pursued by creditors, after squandering his fortune.

Daniel Defoe was my week-thirty-five reading (the 'little ball' given by Roxana in the eponymous novel). He had what would these days be termed a 'portfolio career': he was variously a merchant, a tax accountant, a ship insurer, a pamphleteer, propagandist and secret agent. He took part in a couple of rebellions, was captured by Barbary pirates, went bankrupt and was imprisoned several times: all of which gave him the perfect pedigree to write his last book,

The Compleat English Gentleman. In his spare time he also invented the English novel. I, by comparison, am merely a party promoter who runs a shop and gallery on the side. If Defoe could successfully combine all those activities in addition to his literary career, why not me? I think it was at this point that I added to my deadline burden by deciding to organize a party for six hundred people on the weekend I was due to give birth and deliver my manuscript.

I was by now well into my third trimester (by this stage I reckoned my flesh and blood baby must weigh more than my paper and cardboard one would – even if the latter had embossed gold lettering on the jacket) and I decided I would have to take advantage of my decreased mobility to sit down and tackle some of the weightier authors I had been putting off.

Thomas Pynchon was first on my list. His 1973 novel *Gravity's Rainbow* contains several parties, but I wondered how such a notorious recluse as Pynchon could write about having a social life. Or had his lack of profile enabled him to do all of the necessary literary research incognito, including the party I write about in my book: an orgy aboard a yacht called the *Anubis*?

In week thirty-six I got round to Proust (the Marquise de Saint-Euverte's musical soirée in *Swann's Way*). *In Search of Lost Time* is of course a highly appropriate topic for an author approaching their deadline. It's the question we all ask ourselves: where on earth did all that time go when I should have been writing? For most writers a lot of it was probably spent drinking cups of tea or coffee. Proust, I discovered, was a caffeine junkie. In one famous session a Parisian host recalls him knocking back seventeen cups of coffee in a single evening, I read jealously (one of the things I missed while pregnant was my morning hit of espresso). Proust's caffeine habit may have explained his manic inability to express himself in brief sentences. The longest sentence in *In Search of Lost Time* clocks in at a brain-numbing 942 words.

Week forty was looming and I had put off the toughest author, Joyce, and his toughest work, *Finnegans Wake*, till last. By this stage I was hoping that my baby would be late, because with 628 pages of macaronic prose to digest, my book was definitely going to be. I really should have known my biology better. My first daughter had been born on her due date and so was my second, at exactly forty weeks. Needless to say, I missed my own party. It was only a few days later that I realized the final irony. Baby Una was born on June 16th – Bloomsday, the day on which all the action takes place in Joyce's other big novel, *Ulysses*. Obviously she had a keen sense of irony, as well as a knowledge of the classics – so it didn't matter that I hadn't done all the in-utero hothousing after all.

Most authors who miss their deadline get a telling off from their publishers. I got flowers from mine.

ANNIE FREUD

Forty

I drew this picture to avoid
saying anything about forty.

I have always hated numbers.
Thinking about them is torture.

They make me feel I'm going mad.
They are like swastikas to me.

RICHARD HOUSE

From '40 + 1'

Start. Away from LAX the motorway swings wide of the city and rises on concrete stilts. The houses sit in a broad plate that stretches all the way back to a borderline of mountains, box after box after box, low-lying, white and tan. Above the freeway the tops of palm trees bend in the wind, tatty and elegant. In the centre of the plain, fuzzed blue, rise the towers of the downtown skyscrapers, vague and distant and handsome.

First in the van, Kipper sits behind a woman from Florida with his knees shunted up because the seats are too close. She's come to Los Angeles to sit one of three law exams. This recession, she says, speaking to my reflection, is taking money from her pocket.

The downtown hotels are the first drop-off. The driver points out a garage as we pass. He stopped there last week, can't remember why, and one of the passengers jumped out to use the bathroom. He drove off before the passenger could get back in, and didn't realize what he'd done until he was back at LAX hours later and found the man's luggage. The man never showed up and the security camera shows him running toward the freeway, arms going crazy. The company still have his suitcase. No one contacted them, no one complained. He's laughing about this as he tells it, teeth yellow as a dog's. The driver asks again where we're going and I hold out the booking slip which he won't read. Temple and Lansing. The driver insists there's nothing there, but I've paid to go to Temple and Lansing and that's where he'll take me.

The neighbourhood beside City Hall is called Skid Row. Skid Row is on the up and up. The streets twist off the freeway, and down among the concrete legs men dither, slumber, or labour behind shopping trolleys. There are semi-permanent shelters built of cardboard, sooty with exhaust, and multi-coloured one-man tents purpose-designed for the street. Downtown the pavements and walkways are empty, these men sleep close to bright bars and restaurants and public sculptures. The driver points out one man and says that man, right there, you see him *everywhere*, you wouldn't believe how strong he is; and looking at him he's right, we don't believe him. That man is a ghost. Kipper is silent. There are new developments the driver says, Los Angeles isn't as big as you'd think, it's the adjoining towns that make the sprawl appear so massive. It would be larger still if the sea didn't stop it, and one day they'll figure out how to build right over it. Everything changes here.

The driver asks a third time if I'm going to Angelino Heights and I repeat that I don't know what the neighbourhood is called. I hold up the paper then realize he keeps asking because he can't read. That's three stories already. One. Two. Three. Three off forty leaves thirty-seven. Stop.

Start. Kipper wakes me early. He has an idea, he says, and if he doesn't tell it, he'll lose it.

A man wakes up. He's on a train. The train is an express, long distance. It makes no stops. Trans-America or trans-Europe. The man has no memory of getting on the train, had no plans or intention to travel. He's confused. All he knows is that he's woken up, confused, groggy, disorientated, and his right hand is wrapped in a bandage. He goes to the toilet and doesn't recognize the clothes he's wearing: his eyes are bloodshot, his face is drawn, his throat is sore and he's thirsty. After drinking from the tap he bangs his hand, it's sore, so he unwraps the bandage and discovers that two of his fingers are missing.

Nice, I say.

Kip likes that too, but that's not the key part.

The man is so freaked that he gags – a deep, uncomfortable retch, he's almost choking with what's caught in his throat, he coughs up two slimy white pods, condoms, and there in the sink are two tight packets of cocaine. He's being used as a mule. Someone has filled him full of drugs and cut off two fingers either as a warning or to signal him out so someone can recognize him at the station.

And he has no memory of the night before?

Kipper shakes his hand. This can be figured out later. He has no memory, but it's not amnesia, it's drink or drugs. Everything is there but scrambled, noise in his head, so it'll take time to figure out what really happened. The story is chewed up. We have a situation, not unlike the idea of someone waking up in a motel and finding a scar across their abdomen and their kidney has been stolen, but a little more urgent. The mention of the motel makes us both aware of the room. I've been listening to planes land all night, the slow falling swoop, the after-burn fading into the gentle burr of the traffic. Behind the motel is a broad parking lot, and behind that, the freeway. The room isn't so bad, the size of it, pink foot-worn carpet, a double bed, orange curtains, a kind of muslin, thick enough to stop anyone seeing in, but coarse enough to spangle the sunlight which hits the glass early. There's a constant haze in the room, like someone has been smoking, but it's nothing more than dust.

Can you work with it?

I'm interested. I'm sitting up. It's a smart idea. I like it. It's a strong idea, it isn't going to evaporate under examination. Ideas are fragile. Tell it to the wrong person and it's gone. Tell it in the wrong way and you're left wondering why it fascinated you.

This is our seventh idea. We have six days. Our target is forty ideas. Good. Bad. It doesn't matter. This new idea is a keeper. It doesn't sound too much like anything I can think of, which raises its value. The worst idea is about a girl with a beard. We don't know what to do with her yet, but she's nine years old, has this fantastic beard, and she lives chained-up in a kennel. Dog-beard-girl.

This is Kipper's seventh idea in two days. If we needed proof that coming here was a good idea, that's it right there. Seven ideas in two days, that's one idea every seven hours, which sounds slack if you compare it with sewing clothes, building walls, fruit-picking, or working behind a bar, but if you think about the amount of books, or films, or stories, or treatments that one person is ever going to write, then one solid idea every seven hours is a good pace. My contribution is in the detail and development. There are different kinds of ideas people, different kinds of ideas, different means of development.

I ask him if he dreamt this, and he says yes, more or less. It came to him in one of those in-between moments, when you're kind of waking and there it is, bobbing up in the last anxiety of sleep.

We eat at the A&T, a small diner on the corner of Union, because it's cheap, because it's just across the road, and because of the hash browns are fried in butter or pork fat, but really we come here because the police and firemen also love this place, and both of us get a kick out of sitting ten feet or closer to a man with a gun. The idea is to see how close we can sit to a man with a handgun. If you aren't used to seeing a man with a gun, then you probably understand the urge to want to touch the gun, especially if the man with the gun is doing something normal like chewing, sipping coffee, picking at his teeth, or otherwise not paying attention to the gun at his hip. Touching the gun, actually setting your hands on it is one of those things you're pretty certain you won't do, but you can't trust yourself enough to say you'd never do it, because it's there in your head, and like most ideas, they become a little bit more likely to happen once you've thought them.

This isn't whimsy, but a fully-fledged notion.

You want to touch it. The gun. You want to grab it out of the holster, jump on the table, one foot in the cop's breakfast burrito, and tell everyone to get down, get under the tables, and there, right there, with the cool jets of a leaky air-conditioner fleecing goose-bumps down your neck you take out the windows one by one. After that you're buggered, because there are many other police officers whose responses are going to be speedy, automatic, and who knows what's happened with those bullets because there's plenty of traffic out there and someone's bound to get hurt. A pregnant mother or something, or worse, someone like Amy, or a woman who is just about to invent something, like a cure for ass-cancer derived from some simple household product (crushed aspirin and mouthwash), and she's just having this idea when one of your bullets ricochets off the stoplight and goes right in through her left temple. It doesn't kill her, it's much worse, your actions leave her in a permanently vegetative state where this unfinished idea goes continually rattling around, unstoppable and incomplete: she's left thinking *aspirin, mouthwash, aspirin, mouthwash* for the rest of her life unable to put the two together. That's the irony, because the streets and boulevards aren't going to be piled up with bad guys, like every neighbourhood creep is standing shoulder on shoulder in a human pyramid right at the intersection, because it's not that kind of a fantasy. This is one of those fantasies with some major underlying guilt.

Kipper agrees, it wouldn't happen like that, there would be a bus full of school-kids outside, and you'd cap two of them in the jaw, and they'd be bleeding and dying and you'd have to watch them feeling regret, understanding just how feeble the word sorry is. Sorry is a word for polite accidents, for little things. It just doesn't work with anything big. There has to be an idea in that.

And here it comes. Tomorrow my sister is fifteen years old and I'm not going to see her. I'm not going to see Amy today or tomorrow or any time soon.

The gun idea was Kipper's. What would it be like to shoot one of those things? Right here? Why not? What would that be like? I guess that right there is an example of an idea that comes out of one person and goes to another so you don't know in the end whose idea it is, although you might be able to name the origin of it. What it needs is a shape.

Idea thirty-eight: a man runs away to Los Angeles. In two days he walks the entire length of Wilshire Boulevard. Plan A, come up with forty ideas for books, for stories, for films. Plan B, take out life insurance just in case this doesn't work.

Idea thirty-nine: Kipper isn't real. Never was.

Idea forty: A man goes to sleep and dreams he knows that he is dreaming, but what troubles him is that he seems to be misreading everything. For example, the air is full of missiles and because he's floating, he's not sure whether the missiles are heading toward him or if he is heading toward the missiles. Only when it's too late does he realize that this is immaterial, because the question he should be asking himself is: *what is likely to happen when everything collides?* He should be thinking about getting out of the way, or better still, of waking up. But no, he's too busy thinking of the wrong thing so he'll never wake up. Stop.

JACKIE KAY

Owl

It was when I was ten and Tawny was nine that we first came across the barn owl on the farmland where our parents went that summer on holiday. We think they went on one last holiday to work out their future, because we heard the four of them whispering often, sometimes furiously. But the noise that stayed with us through our childhood and into our teens was the screech of the barn owl. We gave each other nicknames that night as if to remember, and they stuck well past our forties. I was Barn and she was Tawny. Tawny and Barn. We thought it made us sound like a pair of detectives like Starsky and Hutch, or a pair of comedians like Eric and Ernie. We started dressing in similar clothes. We bought sleuth sweaters. Our parents often took holidays together but this was the first one where we actually noticed that Tawny's father seemed happy chatting to my mother and that my father seemed to laugh in a different way with Tawny's mother.

We always imagined that owls hooted. It was only after that strange holiday on the farm, with the fields and fields of rolled bales of hay and the red tractor and the big jugs of milk fresh from the black-and-white cows and the rows of green, muddy wellington boots outside the porch, and the potatoes that we were allowed to dig up ourselves, that we realized that owls could screech too. And when we got back home and looked up barn owl, we gasped. Tawny said, 'The barn owl is also known as the screech owl,' and I said 'No!' 'We said it screeched, didn't we!' Tawny said, excited and proud. 'We did. We named it before the encyclopaedia got there!' 'Weird, isn't it,' Tawny said. 'Weirder and weirder,' I said, which was our phrase for everything that was happening around us. We actually saw Tawny's father kiss my mum one night when we'd crept out late to watch the night flights of our barn owl. When we got back into bed breathless and terrified, all we could whisper was, 'Weirder and weirder,' and giggle ourselves helplessly to sleep.

'We actually managed to make friends with an owl,' we told our friend when we got back to school. 'How?' Sandra Clark asked, sceptical. 'We brought it things to eat?' 'What things?' she said, her eyes narrowing like her mother's, exactly like her mother's. 'A frog.'

'A frog? I don't believe you!' she said. And for some reason this made her burst into tears. I think she burst into tears because before that summer she had been Tawny's best friend; and Tawny and I returning with new nicknames and tales of our feathered friend made her feel left out. (Well, she wasn't actually there.) 'Two's company, three's a crowd,' we'd always say to the third of the moment, leaving her or me or Tawny alone and miserable for at least a few hours, which felt like days. 'I don't believe you fed a frog to an owl,' Sandra said. 'But why would we lie about something like that?' I said. 'Why lie that you'd fed an owl a frog?'

'So you can say you've done something I haven't,' Sandra said, wiping away her tears.

'That wasn't all we fed the owl,' I continued. Sandra sucked in her cheeks and flicked back her hair. She looked demented. 'What else?' she said, challenging me, her eyes full of hurt and fury. 'We caught a wild rabbit and brought it to our barn owl,' I said. 'Didn't we?' I said to Tawny. Tawny didn't answer. 'Oh, that's just rubbish, just rubbish,' Sandra said and stalked off and Tawny and I split our sides laughing. We couldn't stop. It was painful. 'Sandra's getting so boring,' I said to Tawny and Tawny said 'She's all right,' which made me feel miserable and worried.

'I don't think we should both be called after the owl,' Tawny said to me the next day, 'or else we need a name for Sandra too. Like Feathers or something.'

'But she wasn't there,' I said. 'She never brought the owl a rabbit!' I was outraged. 'You've got to earn your nickname!'

'But *we* never brought the owl a rabbit.'

'But *she's* not to know that!' I said. 'Anyway, we did really because we did it in our head.'

That was when we had a big talk about whether things

that happened in your head were real or not: if they could be really real because they happened in your head. I'd already imagined quite a gory and glorious and gut-wrenching scene where our big barn owl gobbles a wild rabbit whole, and it'd hurt me to visualize it so vividly. I'd cried reading *Watership Down*! I'd already kept myself awake at night imagining our barn owl eating a rodent. I'd even just learnt the word rodent in order to say it with complete authority. (I had. I had said to Sandra, 'Did we tell you about the day our owl ate a rodent?' And Sandra had stared aghast and said, 'What's a rodent?' 'A rodent is a rat,' I'd said. I'd been expecting her to ask what a rodent was and I couldn't stop smirking.)

'If you'd known he was such a rat, would you have wasted these years?' That was the question Tawn was asking me now.

'This is what old friends do at our age,' Tawn said, wryly. 'They start going back over their years.'

'Or they sit around and remember their owls,' I said. We both laughed and I somehow managed to avoid the question. Late that afternoon, we drifted off for forty winks. We drifted awake too. It wasn't sudden, but slow. A slow realization that there we were still sitting next to each other, comfortably, after all these years. 'Do you remember Feathers?' Tawn asked me. 'She never knew she was lucky she never saw what we saw.' I wasn't even surprised any more when Tawn and I thought about the same thing at the same time; we'd been doing that for years. 'I was just remembering her.'

I might have even been dreaming her. 'And I was dreaming about that barn owl.'

'Our owl!' Tawn said fondly. 'Our clever owl.'

'What are you going to do?' she asked me.

'Get a place of my own,' I said without a moment's hesitation.

'They say that life begins at forty anyhow!' I said gamely.

'Well, that makes you only ten,' Tawn said laughing. 'And it makes me nine,' she said.

'And there was me waiting to feel grown-up, middle-aged. I still feel like a girl.'

'You still *are* a girl!' Tawn said.

'I thought you said only lesbians stayed girls? And that only heterosexual women grew properly middle-aged?'

'Did I say that?' Tawn said. 'Really? Well then you're not really a proper heterosexual.'

'I'm with a man.'

'Not for much longer!'

'But that doesn't mean I want to be with a woman,' I said. I could feel my hackles rising, like ruffled feathers.

'Do you remember that time when we became convinced we were growing feathers on our arms?' she said, after a brief pause. (Sometimes it seemed Tawn knew me better than I knew myself.)

'Yes, and we thought that soon we'd fly!' I said, swallowing hard.

'And we stood at various parts of the garden and tried to take off?'

'Once I saw my mum kiss your dad.'

'Once I saw my dad kiss your mum.'

It was quite a confusing time. Hard to believe it was forty years ago. I looked at the clock. 'It's late enough now for us to have our gin.'

'Where do you get all these rules from?' Tawn said.

'The middle-aged love rules!' I said. 'They like them more than the young or the old.' I poured us both a gin, chuckling, chucked some ice in and some lime. We always used to like making up untrue facts.

'You'll be fine,' Tawn said. 'You've no idea how free you'll feel.'

'You're on the open road now,' she said. I gulped down my gin. I couldn't imagine my nights. I couldn't think what the nights would be like, locking up downstairs, taking the dog out for the last walk and then locking up, bolting the door.

'You're not going to feel anything like the fear you've been feeling,' Tawn said. 'There's nothing like the fear you feel when you are in the wrong life.'

'How do you know these things?' I asked her.

'Because I'm an owl. You are too.'

'And we were never even in the Brownies!' I said.

'Nope, nor the . . . what was the other ones called, the ones you could progress to?'

'Can't remember,' I said. 'They wore blue uniforms.'

'It'll come back. This is the kind of thing that happens to

forty- and fifty-year-olds even when they are only nine or ten.'

'I know. Scary. Suddenly forgetting things.'

'It's only scary because we all want to be perfect. It's not scary if we just don't care,' Tawn said.

'But it's the feeling of things slipping out of your control, the idea that we might suddenly just lose it, lose our minds.' I could feel a note of hysteria creeping into my voice. I was only half joking.

'We've everything to live for and nothing; that's what you realize when you are forty.'

'That you're at least halfway there?'

'Nope. You realize that you're starting to turn back.'

'Maybe that's why I can't stop thinking about that summer when we found out our mums and dads had swapped.'

'We never talked about it at the time.'

'Do you think it did our heads in?'

'Well, it wasn't exactly calming. It didn't make us feel settled.'

'Do you remember the night of the owl?' Tawn said. I nodded. We hadn't ever talked about that either. Not in excruciating detail. But now that we'd agreed I was ten and she was nine, exactly the ages we were then, it seemed we must. We must face what we saw and what we did about what we saw. And maybe after that we could go back to our names, to calling ourselves our real names. (Though I doubt we'd ever do that. It would sound like we were angry at

each other, or suddenly frosty if I out of the blue started calling Tawn Marion and she started calling me Anita. It'd be
ridiculous. Our names would sound dated.) 'I could never
call you anything other than Tawn,' I said, before we began
the frightening work of piecing together the night of the owl.
'Strange, don't you think, that we don't really connect our
nicknames to the owl any more?'

'After a while, I don't think you connect any name to anything any more. It just is,' Tawn said. She had this way of
explaining everything so that everything made perfect sense.

'Do you think you need to drag things up before you can
move on?' I asked her. Just thinking about returning was
making me feel sick.

'Do you know what?' Tawn said, and her voice sounded
elated. 'We don't need to. We don't need to do it. If we don't
want to talk about it, we don't have to. Our life has just
begun. This is the new one we're in.'

'The past will always try and drag you back,' I said, miserably.

'Not if you don't want it to,' Tawn said. 'Come on, Barn,
let's just move on. Let us just do it. Move on. They don't
deserve us.'

The next morning we both woke up feeling as if we'd
released something in the night. 'Shall we go for a walk?' I
asked. I didn't want her to leave. We walked to the end of
my street and turned left. Then we walked on the meadows
for miles. By the Mersey, we saw a heron stand religiously

still for some time before taking off, taking flight, its huge wings opening and closing, opening and closing.

The heron reminded me of the wonder we felt as girls watching our owl take off into the starry sky, dive down and come back again, how we soared with it, how we roared when we heard its screech, how our lives felt so up in the air; how, when we imagined something, we became it, effortlessly. 'We had huge wings, didn't we, Tawn? I said, a little sadly, the river slow beside me. 'You're starting to sound very middle-aged,' Tawn said. 'Remember you're only ten. And you do still have wings. You're going to need them any time soon.'

IAN KELLY

Forty Photographs

If memory is what we thought we'd forgotten then history is
what we can't forget.

- Two ginger boys in fancy dress. Twin dice, heads
  and arms and legs sticking out of boxes. The smell
  of crêpe paper and the scrape of staples. A photo
  does exist, from the ship's photographer. I don't
  think I properly remember the occasion – apart from
  the box rubbing my legs, and that we didn't win the
  competition. Or perhaps everyone won.

- Embarkation. New York City, the colours of *Kojak*
  and Kodak: acid yellows, lilac kipper ties. My
  father's sideburns.

- The flotsam and the seagulls on the Hudson, when I
  was held up to our porthole window.

- The view over the side to the spuming Atlantic ten

storeys below me, and an irrefutable desire to fall towards the blackening water.

- The slapping of the decktop pool's brine, over my head, salt water in my nostrils.
- Hydrangeas, a matronly swimcap of a flower, in a suburban garden. Fresh and novel to an English boy returning to an England he had never seen.

Photographs are the least reliable historical sources. Like memories, they have a reputation for emotional exactitude, when, in fact, they lie. Shocking to find this album of snapshots is now curled at the edges of forty years. It's impossible to know anymore which are real and which have simply developed over the years in the darkroom of the mind and the retelling of stories: *'What was it like? Did you wave goodbye to the Statue of Liberty? Is it true there is a pool on board?'*

I try for corroboration from the yellowing photographs or from my brother or my parents sometimes, but the images are refrains in the family song; repeated so you notice not the words but the rhythm, comforting and meaningless.

———

Southampton docks in the early 1970s cannot have been lovely. Presumably not, as they laughed when I said it was. Nor was my kindergarten opinion just an early-learned anxiety to please – my new country, my new relatives – it was a photographic truth without a negative: Southampton *was* beautiful to my American eyes. Of the album of real and imagined childhood memories – most from family folklore or from other people's photographs, this one stands out as a rare impression on the mind of childhood. It must be real. There could be no photos to misremember by. No image of a lilac hydrangea in a dockside garden, viewed first from the boat and then again as we sped along a suburban Southampton road in a hire-car on the wrong side of the road; *'Can we see England now?'*

Forty years ago families travelling all together did not fly the Atlantic. They crossed the water in time-zone increments and inclement weather, the last generation of ocean-going huddled masses with trunks hauled over quaysides and a floating neverland between one home and another: a ship-bound world of cabins and stewards and limitless food. And for a small child, perforce, an Atlantic crossing was an utter caesura between one country and another, an old home and new one, with a blinding flashback of ocean spray and sun-blasted deck-quoits to mark the meridian in memories. Every day they turned the clock forward an hour, an incomprehensible ritual to me at the time, but impressive all the same: adults reorganizing time, so that each day was its own independent time zone, floating between continents, ploughing east. Grown-ups can rearrange time.

The return to England is not my first memory, but it was strange enough to force the deep impression that all that had come before was over. The maple-syrupy American Christmasses, and the sunny country-club years of my parents' marriage – these were memories that sloped one way into the oblivion of pre-history and the cradle, but decline in the other direction as the forty years of my life as an English-man, measured from that moment we stepped ashore at Southampton. Everything was grey but the flowers, which were abundant: exuberant daubs in gardens everywhere; purple and lilac hydrangeas and roses against pebbledash – the new textures and colours of England.

We sold all our toys forty years ago, arraigned on a low garden wall in Chestnut Hill. My brother's Tonka toys and our red wagon, my tricycle and my embarrassment of puppets and dolls. The sun shone and the neighbours came and went. My dressing up things and 'the figures' – the little paper dolls I used for puppet shows but secretly adored for the simple beauty of the clothes and the way they fleshed out my stories – were tidied away by my mother. We squeezed our entire family life into one ocean-going container, and lived at a neighbour's house with a suitcase each, that last sultry Philadelphia summer, and said goodbye to our dog. Murph was too old for the Atlantic, and for quarantine. My brother cried, but my heart was more malleable, and my ambitions set ahead, on English time. I could not, I declared – and this I know as I can see the suburbs skimming past the car window and feel the indentation of hard VW upholstery on shortlegged trousers – I could not recall how I had made the friends I had, so would find out how it was done. In England. America disappeared into the very start of consciousness: for me, there was no 'before'. For my parents, I think I could see even then, it was different, but I may be redrafting history and memory. The end of an adventure of emigrating, perhaps, for them. The end of their campus and Updike years. Certainly for us, the end of our trick-or-treat American boyhood. For them, the beginning of a recession and the retrenchment into their forties, which in those days was middle age. America, a book of genesis on what their aspirations for us had been, followed by years of recrimination and regret or just the slow corrosive drip of nostalgia. For Dad, I suspect, it was never so good again.

I have no memory of my father on the boat, or getting off. I recall his stressful distraction in New York, and driving up from Philly, my brother and me cradled in the back of a U Haul van with trunks like haystacks all around us. One fell on me. The scar is forty years old. He took us to the Rockefeller Center. I know I actually remember this, rather than being told or seeing the photo, as I can see the statue of Atlas in my mind's eye, not quite managing to shrug off the globe we were about to ship across, but I have never seen a photograph, and did not know where the memory came from properly until I was back in New York as a young man. My dad was famously ill-equipped on the high seas, I think he kept to the cabin whilst my brother, the precocious one, plunged into life on deck, made pals with stewards and challenged other kids to deck quoits whilst I trailed in his wake, practising my new British accent. There was a library on board, a plush and hushed temple of books where my mother read us stories and we could borrow what we liked, sitting cross-legged on the carpet as the ship swayed to the smell of shoe leather and the touch of paper.

I didn't learn to read or write for some while after all that. A late starter, I now discover, who worried my parents accordingly. But now I write for a living, or at any event, write to forge sense with lives borrowed from others, as best I might, as a biographer. Measuring the angles either side of those peripetiae, the turning points, in others' lives, I only rarely consider a few of mine. A fortieth birthday forces that upon us, though not my own. A little while after we returned, my younger brother was born, which rearranged in other ways the family geography. He is about to be forty, which is pause for thought for the baby of the family, but also for all of us who thoughtlessly labelled him as such. Forty years' worth of memories: now that's a valid distance from which to begin to see the lie of the land. The Atlantic seems to feature widely. It is the crossing my life hinges over. American girlfriends, nearly emigrated for. A year straight after school, the first oxygen of freedom and manhood. Back on the East Coast, dutifully writing letters to make sense of it all. All biography begins with autobiography. An American postgraduate sentence, which really began the habit of writing, and the ambition, not to mention the displacedness, that is the sentence of a writer I suspect.

Aunty Jo had come to meet us. Do I remember having her pointed out, waving on the quayside, or have I only been told so? And if I did say I could see her, it would only have been to please my mother and attach to the mooring reality of this ocean-vast love in her life. Uncle John was there too. Sharp-elbowed and bespectacled. I do clearly remember meeting my grandmother, Nanny, whom I had never seen, crying great rolling tears of joy that pooled in the creases of a powdered cheek as she pressed a small stranger to her shoulder, and the dusty smell of lavender soap. I don't think, forty years on, there has ever been a deeper impression on me of the pain of separation, or of parenthood. Nanny and Aunty Jo had come to see my brother and me, figures from Christmas-card photographs till then, but a child notices attention, or the lack of it, and their eyes were fixed not on us, but on my own mother, her homecoming-attempt at American glamour immediately crumpled in the warm embrace of her own mother and sister. And she appeared thus instantly to me, in the flashbulb of a new reality, and for the very first time, forty years ago, as more than the lodestar of my little life, but as someone else's child.

Which was why I was looking studiously out of the window, I suspect, forty years ago as we drove out of Southampton, and why the hydrangea in a terraced garden seared onto the retina of memory: an irrelevant detail and not even a truly eye-catching one. It turns out not to be in the album anywhere. Why would it be? It turned out to have safer archiving elsewhere.

GAVIN KNIGHT

The Forty Years War

I gave my wife the number of a social worker to call if anything went wrong; she asked who I was meeting; I didn't say
he was a convicted killer.

Calum was waiting awkwardly, in a grey mac, hunched
over an ageing Nokia. He was slightly stooped, baffled by
the mini-blackboard of specials, the spicy cakes and exotic
bread and the sashaying waiters with angular facial hair.
This was Merchant City, Glasgow's version of Covent
Garden. We chose two chicken pies with mash.

He was recently out of Glasgow's notorious Barlinnie
jail, which I'd visited twice that week. The wall was higher
than the one in *King Kong*. If you could throw a bundle of
drugs over that you should be in the Olympic team. Inside it
was like a row of ugly red-brick churches. A queue of uni-
formed inmates twitched towards their green beakers of
syrupy methadone. The cheery, rotund governor unlocked

one of the outer doors so we could march through the wings; galleries looked down on us just like in *Porridge*. At the end he showed me the showers: a very dangerous place for attacks, he said. They were dark and narrow like the gap behind a wardrobe.

Calum was a little manic. His train of thoughts crisscrossed in their eagerness to come out, so much he had to get across. With his ruffled pate, bald crown and high-pitched laugh there was the air of an eccentric poet or academic about him. Sectarianism was a big thing in Glasgow, he said, and showed me his mobile phone: the crossed-rifles emblem of the UVF, Ulster Volunteer Force. He grinned like a child sharing a risqué joke.

Later we walked through the Barras, the Celtic heartland, which was all quaint Irishness of gothic-script pubs and shamrocks.

'I'd come down here off my head on coke looking for a fight,' he smiled. 'I'd wear a balaclava and put a machete down the back of my shorts.' The shorts seemed the maddest touch. Soon we came to the featureless streets of the Calton, one of the poorest wards in Britain, where life expectancy is lower than the Gaza Strip. Across the street local kids outside the chip shop scowled us up. They were almost translucently thin, shaven heads like billiard balls, their shell suits draped off their collarbones like wire hangers. It was notorious for heroin and prostitutes in the eighties, Calum told me, young runaways mainly, strung out and under threat from the punters. His family home was total junkie chaos. He's one of the first generation of kids who grew up with drug-addicted parents; toddlers opening the front door to strangers who were coming in to shoot up, deal or whatever. It was 1971 that the Misuse of Drugs Act was brought in. It is officially a forty-years war.

For the cops in the trenches it is a war of attrition. It sucks up resources. Days spent in parked-up hire cars, staking out teenage street-level shotters in buy-or-bust operations that might result in a conviction for possession but the kingpins at the top remain untouched. The UK drug trade has far greater revenues than Tesco and infinitely more outlets. In the sprawling Stonebridge Estate in Brent, London, the police put a handful of undercover cops into a tower block for months to infiltrate one group of dealers. The ringleader sat inside watching dealings on his own laptop via surveillance devices. After the operation the tower blocks were razed to the ground and low-rises brought in. One of the few people to escape Stonebridge was Maria Lawson, who did so well on the second series of *X Factor* she moved to Canary Wharf. There are four ways out of the ghetto: *X Factor*, boxing, education and drug-dealing. I met a twenty-year-old girl who dealt drugs to buy clothes for her acting auditions. Another girl stole a stash to afford her mother's medication. Another teenager put himself through college on his drug sales. The malevolent Olders take time to coach the most dynamic young kids in the inner city as their new apprentices, outlining their career progression more intricately than any McKinsey or Goldman Sachs sophomore. Sometimes dealers even extend help to the community – an alarming development that sees the UK drifting towards the Brazilian gang model.

It's forty years since the Misuse of Drugs Act and it hasn't even undergone an independent assessment. Thatcher's evidence-based approach was better than Blair's moralizing one but ultimately drug policy has to be signed off by Paul Dacre, editor of the *Daily Mail*. There are far more innovative strategies out there: in New York they have special drug courts, in Portugal they have a panel that focuses on dissuasion. In Castlemilk, Glasgow, a nursery deals with drug-addicted parents at the same time as it is developing their toddlers' emotional playtime. Calum and his sister became addicted early on. Like them, there are 350,000 children growing up in the UK with drug-addicted parents.

It was dark now as we wandered deeper into the East End into Barrowfield. A notorious heroin hub in the eighties, it was still one of the most dangerous schemes; social workers even today aren't allowed into it without a police escort. In the street Calum ran into an acquaintance; I hung back as they exchanged small talk but it was too cold to linger. It was after midnight and I couldn't see any buses any more. We seemed to have strayed from the main road, through back gardens peopled by groups of kids. At the peak of the epidemic, Calum told me, the gangs stopped fighting as they were too busy selling off their gear. One night the drug-fuelled chaos of Calum's upbringing took its toll. Off his head as a teenager, he fell into a brawl with another youth. He chased him onto a nearby building site. As they fought his opponent slipped and struck his head hard on the ice. Calum slowed as he told me, his breath silver under the street lamps. The other kid died that night; Calum went to prison for culpable homicide – it's a crime specific to Scottish law, which means he didn't mean to kill him. Murders are all about young men: stoned or drunk young men. The bulk of the murders, assaults and domestic violence cases in Glasgow are committed with drugs or alcohol in the bloodstream. Our chat had brought us a long way from Merchant City with its mannequins tightly wrapped in Italian fashion. He revealed he had a teenage daughter who worked in a shop in the centre. He said he hoped to be more in her life now he was clean. A yellow light appeared in the distance and hummed towards us. I hailed the driver. I shook Calum's hand and he was gone.

BELINDA McKEON

Forty of You

Freckles on your knuckles. Briar-cuts on your legs. Cipeens packed into the hot press. "Go fish, little ducky. Go fish!"

*

You were Dutch, I think. You were Hans, I think. In our school for a term, or maybe only a month. You had to walk the path one day, as a punishment, and I walked it with you. Solidarity. Or obsession. Then you went back to wherever you came from. This is twenty-seven years ago.

*

As for you. The other day, I had to sign a book for your father. The things I was tempted to write.

*

Star-child. They said you wouldn't learn to use your words. Keep doing that. Keep proving them wrong.

*

I did not steal your sock.

*

Such excitement as we left for the church on your wedding day, we forgot to check that you were with us. Someone looked in a rear-view mirror and saw you standing in the lane. Waving us down.

*

What can I say? Where can I begin? In the photographs from the beginning, you look like a child yourself. And then there is a photograph of the three of us at Elfeet. My father holding his sunglasses to my face. Both of you lit up with smiles.

*

I remember the night and the Tennessee Waltz.

*

I google you the odd time. Where the hell have you disappeared to? Christ, you were a lunatic.

*

Red-topped moppet. Muck on your face. Mischief in your

eyes. I copied you for a baby in a book; I think I've mentioned that a couple of times.

*

And you: you're a cat. That makes no difference.

*

You walked into a philosophy class on the first day of college, and I had never seen anyone so beautiful. It was outrageous. Years later, an email from you – affectionate – "Look, just stay out of trouble, all right?"

*

All right.

*

Grandmother. I heard your voice very clearly, not long ago. Nothing like that has happened to me before. I don't know what you were saying. I suppose I should have written it down. But it was the sound of you. I'd forgotten.

*

Our Leaving Cert year. You, yawning and brooding up the top of a clattering school bus. I thought you looked like Noel Gallagher. And I thought, somehow, that this was a good thing.

*

I saw you this morning, in the cafe on Dawson Street where you sit every day. You were in your seat by the window; you'd nodded off for a while. It's deep into winter now. Stay warm. *"And time ran out, and everything changed colour in its wake."*

*

Well, look. Not everyone will punch the life out of an elevator in your honour.

*

May 1991. And if you hadn't come along, what way would the rest of us be by now?

*

Dear Sebastian Dangerfield, yrs ever so, Maudlin Gonne.

*

In your house of paintings, your house full of the books that taught me to care about books at all, in your house with the dogs and the clay pots and the silk scarves, you are in pain. And I don't know what to do for you.

*

"An altar dignifying the god of chance. / What is beautiful, it cautions, / is found accidentally and not sought after. / What is beautiful is easily lost." Charles Simic, "The Altar"

*

Serendipity. You said it. What does it mean again?

*

64 Morehampton Road. Someone's turn to make the tea.

*

One night in a car park in Galway, it dawned on me that my brother was also my friend.

*

The sitting room in your house up the lane; your tall-backed chair. Wimbledon on the television, and me, a runaway from the work of hedge-trimming, sitting at your feet, a glass of lemon barley water in my hand. A frantic knocking on the front door: my mother, in a rage with me. She's been searching everywhere, she tells me; even in the bogholes. Even at five, I can tell this is melodrama. I look at you. You arch a brow.

*

That was your grandmother, in that sitting-room, in front of that tennis match. It would have done you good to know her. Are you going to be all right?

*

What you enjoy: a ribbing about your politics, or a scrap of gossip about someone on television, or a story from a wedding or a funeral, where somebody knew somebody who knew somebody you knew. You want to go to Las Vegas. I can see you running wild from one hectic bank of lights to another.

*

Wise eyes that saw everything. What would you make of us now?

*

I haven't met you yet. Your father says you're going to be amazing. No pressure.

*

You too.

*

This April, you'll walk the aisle. I'll be in front of you, in a dress of taupe, or palomino, or sand. Smiling like a maniac. Something in my eye.

*

Down the line from Tinley Park, Illinois: the gentlest voice I know.

*

The brilliant, teeming head on you. The whistle-stop wicked tongue. The heart on you. The size of it.

*

"You are mostly being studious, I can tell. No little hint of gin chat at all. I do hope it's going well, and if you should ever feel like nipping out of the torture chamber, I am rather in the mood for getting v v drunk."

*

Evenings, the two of us walking home from the Lecky to someone else's house. Our own homes to go to. Wanting only to be elsewhere.

*

His slow movements around the kitchen. Fixing more drinks so that it could not yet be time for anyone to go. Light in his eyes: his son was home.

*

Your mother went suddenly one day, early into a new year. She left you her airmiles. You've travelled the world trying to find her again.

*

"Well chick. You on the mountain this weekend?" (The mountain is not a ski resort in upstate New York. The mountain is a farm on a hill in Leitrim. We are the women who married its sons, and we go there only with back-up.)

*

Please stand clear of the closing doors.

*

And then – how did I get this lucky? – there's you.

CHARLOTTE MENDELSON

Hungarian in Forty Words and Phrases

Magyar – *mog*-yor (Hungarian)

My maternal grandparents were Hungarians. Or so we thought.

They spoke Hungarian, impenetrably, to each other. When speaking English, even after fifty years in London, their Hungarian accents were so strong that kindly strangers would recommend tourist attractions to them. To us, their grandchildren, they seemed entirely, comically Hungarian, whatever that meant: a combination of daring, pride and humour. They were eaters of food composed largely of paprika and garlic; the touchy and ferocious heirs of Dracula and Attila the Hun. We were proud to be temperamentally Magyar; it explained us.

I was in my thirties when I noticed something. My grandmother claimed to be Czech.

Of course I couldn't ask her about it. A central tenet of

Hungarianness, or at least Grandparentness, was the protection of young relatives from any reference to death or sadness and her family history involved too much of both. I knew the name of the nearest town to her village but not how to spell it; there was nothing even close in my school atlas. Years later, I asked a cousin, one of my grandmother's seven sisters' children, who drew me a map on a napkin, although the best match I could find seemed to be in the Ukraine.

Old people make mistakes. The young know best. I continued to refer to her as Hungarian, and to consider myself at least half, although I and my parents were born in England and I have most of the rest of Central Europe in my blood.

But she was growing old. I decided it was my duty to preserve her memories, and solemnly recorded her voice onto audio tape, which I no longer have the means to play. Oddly, she still insisted she was Czech. She spelled the name of her village for me. I decided not to probe.

Then the Internet was invented. I found the napkin, half-remembered the tape and, slowly, with one eye closed to avoid the horrible details, I discovered the extraordinary complexities of her and my grandfather's nationality: born in Czech towns in the Trans-Carpathian mountain region of the Austro-Hungarian Empire, educated in Russian, citizens of extinct Ruthenia, cooking and talking and sounding entirely Magyar but considering themselves simultaneously Hungarian Czechs, grateful Labour-voting English citizens and loyal subjects of the *Kveen*.

Boldog születésnap – '*bull*-dog *soo*-lertaishnop' (happy birthday); **hogy vagy** – *hodge vodge* (how are you?); **paradiscsom** – *porodi*-chom (tomato); **krumpli** – *croom*-pli (potato); **microhulam** – *mee*-cróhulam (microwave)

To infantile English ears, Hungarian sounds ridiculous. Gradually, to amuse my grandparents, I evolved a speciality, a sort of tribute act: I would pretend to order a meal, using as many of my forty words as possible – 'Hello. How are you? Good potatoes! Three tomatoes! No, five! Thank you very much!' – until tears of (I think) laughter ran down my grandmother's cheeks.

On the rare occasions when I meet other children and grandchildren of Hungarians, it is our disbelief in our absurd ancestral language which unites us. We take it in turns to offer our favourite examples of silliness – what sounds like '*ra*-gogoomi' for chewing-gum, or '*boo*-jigo', meaning knickers – and, because all Hungarian grandparents must be as fierce and easily insulted as mine were, it feels excitingly iconoclastic.

For the record, all the passing acquaintances are wrong. The best Hungarian word by far does not mean cherry or perpendicular or deck-chair. It is *kers*-pontifutaysh, technically 'központifűtés': central heating.

Nez – *nayz* (look!); **minden jól** – *meen*-den yol (very good); **természetesen** – *tair*-meseteshen (naturally); **szeretlek** – sair-etleck (I love you); **nodgyon édes!** – *nodj*-yon *ey*-esh! (very sweet); **yoy de édes!** – *yoy* de eydesh! (oh, so sweet!); **yoy** (multipurpose exclamation for use particularly when delighted, or surprised, or worried, or relieved, or sad, or exhausted, or in pain)

Hungarian, as everybody knows, is extraordinarily difficult. No other language will help you understand it; its sole linguistic link is to the Finno-Ugric family, and even this is merely to the extent that if someone is speaking Finnish in another room with the door shut, the inflections will, apparently, sound faintly Hungarian.

Although my grandparents spoke Hungarian to each other and my mother, at its peak my vocabulary never encompassed more than forty words and phrases, none of which I ever learned to spell. Indeed, it barely occurred to me that they could be spelled. Finding them in Hungarian dictionaries has proved difficult: to me they are simply sounds, the background commentary during their weekly visits and our holidays together. I am as astonished as you are by the spellings.

Igen – *ee*-gen (yes); **nem** – nem (no); **egy** – edj (one); **kettő** – *ker*-ter (two); **három** – *ha*-rom (three); **négy** – nedj (four); **öt** – ert (five); **hat** – hot (six); **hét** – hate (seven); **nyolc** – nyolts (eight); **kilenc** – *kee*-lents (nine); **tíz** – tees (ten)

As a determined and conscientious child, I persuaded my grandparents to teach me the numbers one to ten, which I mastered with colossal effort; they seemed proud of my triumph but oddly reluctant to tell me more. Some of their peers forced Hungarian classes and folk-dance lessons on their own grandchildren. Mine did not. They were ambivalent about Hungary, for reasons they did not discuss. Yet, because I miss them and the sound of their voices, I have once or twice heard a tourist or pensioner speaking in that inimitable accent and have rushed to dazzle them with my knowledge. 'Listen!' I say. 'I can do numbers!'

They never seemed quite as impressed as I had hoped.

Macska – *motch*-ko (cat)

Despite my linguistic ignorance I am, at least in one word, bilingual, even actively Hungarian. Whenever I see a cat, I think 'motchko', although my grandparents lived in a flat and did not, as far as I know, like cats.

Köszönöm szépen – *kers*-enem *say*-pen (thank you very much)

My grandmother was fantastically generous: not only with money, or accommodation, or food but also in other, more complicated, ways. She went nowhere without multi-purpose presents: handkerchiefs; glasses cases; chocolates and 'sweeties'; small Czech crystal animals. 'I just give little necklet to Mr X for his vife,' she would say; she left a brooch or a bracelet 'for chambermaid' beside every hotel bed.

When she died we found a vast supply of individually-wrapped tights and gloves and horrible souvenirs, still waiting to be distributed. We also discovered stolen ashtrays, crockery from restaurants she liked and hundreds of biros from neighbouring banks, some with their weighted pen-holder still chained to them.

Popsi – *pop*-shi (bum); **popó** – *po*-po (diminutive; little bum)

As the only grandchildren of an elderly Hungarian woman, our bottoms were not our own. Our grandmother and great-aunts were obsessed with them, pinching and patting them at every opportunity; we would go upstairs protecting them with our hands, usually in vain. They wanted flesh, the old ladies; it was how they measured our health and youth and, I suspect, the passing of their own.

Yet, while startlingly forthright on this and other physical matters – '*vy* do you hide your lovely bosom?'; '*still* your period do not start?'; 'don't you *vant* to look pretty?' – on most physical matters they were silent. Hungarians, at least my Hungarians, if that is what they were, do not swear, or argue in public, or ever, in any circumstance, refer to lavatorial or sexual issues. Ever. My grandmother once became completely hysterical with laughter and embarrassment when I asked her the word for 'buttocks'.

'*Popsi?*'

'No, that's a baby word. There must be another.'

'No! There is not. Really!'

But I insisted, until at last, quite beside herself, she spluttered, '*Popó*'; the rudest word I ever heard her say.

Kavitchka – *kaa*-vitchkó (little coffee); **pongyola** – *pon*-dyuló (dressing gown)

My Hungarian is domestic. I do not know the words for 'sea' or 'train' or 'England', although I have recently discovered that *walesi herceg* means 'Prince of Wales'. If I overheard Hungarians having a sensible conversation, I would understand not a word. All I do know emerged during evenings in the grandparental flat, finding their slippers, fetching orange juice from their minuscule kitchen with the fridge on legs and the persistent scent of paprika. Consequently I have absorbed their bedtime routine to the point where 'to *pondula*' has become a normal-seeming verb.

Palsascinta – *pol*-oshintó (pancake); **paprika** – *pup*-rikosh (paprika); **m'ad artej** – *mod*-arté (*îles flottantes* or floating islands, literally bird's milk)

Most of my vocabulary refers to food. My grandmother cooked like someone in a fairy story. Well into her eighties she would work a six-day week, buy food, drive sixty miles to our house and cook, for example, sour-cherry soup, stuffed peppers, pancakes filled with cream cheese and lemon rind and raisins, and chicken *paprikás* to heat up for tomorrow, and then drive home again, while I moaned about having to clean out the guinea pig. She had a *nokedli* machine, a box with a grater base and a handle into which she would pour batter and extrude little dumplings or noodles into a pan of boiling water below. She had a mincer, and it's her meatloaf and stuffed cabbage I long for now, like grandchildren the world over: hungering for the cheap and labour-intensive food they believe themselves too busy to recreate.

Szervusz – *sare*-vus (hello); **kezét csókolom** – *kez*-et *choc*-olom (children's greeting to older people, literally 'I kiss your hand')

As befits a people whose greeting means 'I am at your service', my grandparents retained a heartbreaking level of formality. They dressed up to go anywhere: the dentist, or the cinema; they ate fruit, including bananas, with a knife and fork. In rare circumstances of extreme relaxation, such as the seaside, my grandfather would wear a vest under his shirt and a cardigan on top, lest chest hair should be revealed. But whereas the English are, or were, merely polite, my grandparents' standards of grooming and manners, even applied to small children, were exhausting. Young people were expected to show their elders the greatest respect, well beyond the courtliness men had to show to women. I still offer my seat to anyone who will let me but, not having grown up in the Austro-Hungarian Empire, other rules remain hazy: should I stand to greet people my age? When an older man approaches a doorway, who lets whom through?

Buta – *boo*-tó (stupid); **csúnya** – *choon*-yó (ugly); **gyenge** – *jen*-ge (weak)

This is not to say that they were always polite. Under

cover of Hungarian, they would comment insultingly on the outfits and characters of relatives, friends and passers-by until they wept with laughter; it was their favourite sport. This went disastrously wrong at the Hungarian Bazaar, an annual event at Porchester Baths in West London, when my grandmother forgot that she could be overheard and understood. Many grudges must have been born that day; not one will have been forgotten.

Mogadon

Hungarian inflections, once absorbed, cannot be forgotten. Mogadon, for example, sounds so silly that I assumed it was a Hungarian word well into adulthood. Now, although my grandfather has been dead for twenty years and my grandmother for six, I still hear, and want to say, certain words in their accent: *mog*-nólyó; *mim*-ósó; *com*-putair; *Vosh*-ington; *rid*-iculos; *Vort*-a-loo; *Coll*-edonió Road, and, most of all, *von*-darefool and *tair*-ible, which was their response to everything, from an unflattering hair cut to regicide.

When asked 'where are you from?' which happens surprisingly often, I hesitate. Despite my strange pre-war BBC accent, my passport, how can I claim to be English when my grandparents spoke as they did? And what do I call them, if not Hungarian?

STUART NADLER

For Phillip, On His Last Night at the Palace

When the first course arrived Phillip realized he was the only person in the restaurant. It was, as it was always on Friday evenings, a fillet of sole simmering in some combination of white wine, chive and butter. He had tried, years ago, to replicate the dish at home, but the exact proportions had proved tantalizingly elusive to him. Han brought the dish out, backing his way through the double doors from the kitchen. Han always brought out Phillip's dishes. Leaning down to lay the plate on the table, he announced it, just as he had done for years. "Sole. Done your way," he said.

Already, Phillip saw evidence of the move. There were boxes where just last Friday there had been a bar. A yellow truck was parked by the kitchen entrance, blocking what had been Phillip's space. This had happened once before, his space occupied by a clunky pomegranate-colored Oldsmobile, and

Margene had dutifully stormed into the restaurant and demanded the thing moved.

The drinks came next. For him, the Blue Tornado, served in a wood-carved tiki cup, a shot of rum poured in at the last moment and then set ablaze for effect. For Margene, as always, a petite cup of Cabernet Blanc, just enough to set her right, but not enough to keep her awake too late. It had been her idea to come here that first time. They had met a weekend earlier at the Perlmutter's, when they lived nearby. She'd made the suggestion, she admitted much later, because she knew the light would be low, and because she was, at that point, still self-conscious about a complexion ravaged by adolescent acne.

Han lingered to be sure the Tornado was to Phillip's liking. There'd been a time, twenty or so years before, when he'd become overly fussy about the grade of rum, and Han, ever the faithful server, still remembered.

"It's very good, Han," Phillip said.

Han smiled, first at him, and then at the glass of Cabernet Blanc. Behind him, a pair of young men came in, shouting in Cantonese, pointing at the tables. One of them, the burlier of the two, picked up a table over his head.

"Forgive me," Han said, backing away. "The truck is early."

At some point over the years, they'd inverted the traditional order of the courses. It had probably been Margene's idea, because, well, most of the things in their life had been

Margene's idea. To have the fish first satisfied their hunger, usually stored up on Friday afternoons when they knew their evenings would end here. Next came the soup, because after the fish, soup seemed nice, and because, as Margene had discovered, having the soup first artificially inflated what remained of their appetite. Or something. By the time Margene had insisted that they do it this way, Phillip had long decided that he would do whatever it was she wanted, in whatever order, on whatever day. This, he decided, was what it meant to love her.

At first it had been called the Garden, then the Cantonese Garden, and then, finally, when another Cantonese Garden opened not so far from here, serving woefully inadequate food and trying to glean some of the class of this original incarnation, Han had changed the name to the Cantonese Palace. This last iteration bore little resemblance to the cozy, charming place Philip and Margene had first encountered, a tiny spot with white table cloths on a street where white table cloths were the norm. To begin, there was the neon on the ceiling. When it was on, Phillip's food seemed to pulsate, an effect, he had decided earlier this year that he did not enjoy. Evidently, there was a stage show on Saturday evenings where, he'd been told, you could enlist a girl, or, if you preferred it, two girls, to dance table-side while you enjoyed your dumplings. Finally, there was the garish fish tank out front, outfitted with sad-looking eel-like creatures that you were encouraged to hand-select and have fried to your liking.

For Phillip, On His Last Night at the Palace

Given the circumstances, Philip could at least entertain the notion that the neighborhood had begun to change. An office park was set to go in where the Foreign Cinema had stood. Where, as it happened, he and Margene had seen *Love In The Afternoon* before eating here for the first time. An Office Park: this is what they called it. Such an unfortunate combination of nouns—two things that had no business existing in such cozy proximity. The day the Cinema closed, Phillip remembered that Margene had cried.

When the soup arrived, Phillip tried to banter with Han. This was their tradition, this bantering and joking. It had been this way since the beginning, when Han was a high-school student nearby, and it was by way of this weekly jousting that Phillip had learned of all the benchmarks in the boy's life: the courtship and eventual marriage to his wife; the birth of his first child; the death of his second child. It sometimes startled Phillip to see Han emerging from the kitchen looking the way he did, which is to say looking nothing like a boy at all.

"Seems like you're keeping your head above water," Phillip said as Han lowered the soup onto his placemat.

Han smiled. "I knew you'd be coming, Mr. Phillip," he said. "So we decided to stay open one last night."

As he backed away, Han eyed the petite glass of Cabernet Blanc, smiling.

The truth was that Margene had never really liked Chinese food. But she'd liked the Garden, as they insisted on calling it, and liked their Friday evenings here, with their first course of fish and their second course of soup, and then, of course, with the fried ice cream that came along with the check. Phillip enjoyed the sensation of eating his ice cream while double-checking Han's math. Even when the Garden upgraded to an adding machine, and then, to a computerized ticketing system, Phillip still did this: a tiny spoonful of fried ice cream and his own arrhythmic, done with the golfer's pencil he carried on the inside pocket of his blazer. This was the beat at the core of his life, these small unbroken rhythms.

He couldn't finish anything anymore. Not his sole, nor his soup, not even his Blue Tornado. Age had ruined his appetite. Or perhaps time had done it. It was difficult to know what bothered him more, growing old or seeing everyone else around him grow old as well.

By now the movers were back, yelling in Cantonese, lifting things above their heads, taking things from the wall. Phillip could hear the sound of a truck backing up outside, that insistent bleating. Looking up, he realized now that all the tables had been removed around him. He hadn't noticed. The carpet in the corners was peeling up, he saw, and there, on the wood, were the telltale marks of a termite's teeth. It was better not to notice some things.

Han emerged through the kitchen door with a silver tray.

"For Phillip," Han said. "On his last night at the Palace."

"What's this?" Phillip asked.

"A treat," Han said, smiling.

Phillip crossed his arms across his chest. "I don't want a treat. I want my ice cream."

Han's smile endured. He lifted the top of the silver tray. It was a framed photograph. Phillip knew the one. Margene was in her white coat. It would be ruined not so long afterward, blood on the lapel, that first hint of trouble. At the time it was taken, the Garden was decorated with photographs of their most loyal customers, and then, slowly, the walls went bare.

"For you," Han said. "To keep."

Phillip shifted in his seat. "This is unnecessary."

Han crouched. "See?" he pointed. "This is Ms. Margene."

"I know who it is."

"And this is you," Han said. He was always smiling. "Looking a little younger, I must say."

Phillip grinned because he knew he ought to grin. His interaction with Han did not include things like this. Presents, and expressions of sentimentality, seemed undignified to him.

Han left the frame standing beside the cup of Cabernet Blanc. A corner of the table reserved for relics, Phillip supposed. Then, Han frowned. "I'm afraid we don't have any ice cream tonight."

Phillip sat up. "No ice cream?"

Han lowered his head. "I'm sorry Mr. Phillip."

"I suppose I'll take the check, then."

Han pointed across the room to the pair of movers. "My men took the register away, already."

"Well give me a written ticket, then."

"It's on me, Mr. Phillip. The meal is on me."

"No. That's not right."

Phillip took out his wallet. By now, he knew the cost of his meal. In forty years of Friday nights, it had been the one thing he had successfully been able to predict. He had been wrong, he knew, about everything else.

"No," Han said, putting a firm hand on Phillip's wallet. "Not tonight."

Phillip leaned back in his chair. The back door was open. Phillip did not know if he'd ever seen the back door open. It was summer outside, but still, he was cold and wished he had a coat.

Later, Han helped him out into the parking lot. This sort of thing had been necessary only the last few Friday nights. All Han did really was to watch him. It wasn't as if he needed someone to hold his hand, the way some of Phillip's acquaintances at the Home needed their hands held when they did things like this, or when they went to the toilet. Walking, so suddenly, had become something to fear, every step accompanied by a sense of doom.

They waited in silence for the van to come. It required, of late, a special dispensation from the Home's oversight board to drop him here on Friday nights, and, an hour and ten minutes later, to pick him up. Especially now with the neighborhood changing, and with the traffic being what it was. No one wanted to come out this way anymore. No one felt safe. The van was always empty. One of the gentlemen's clubs across the road had a neon sign of a woman—her legs opening and closing. Phillip looked at it, looked away, then straightened his necktie.

When the van arrived, the driver lowered the elevated step. Every Friday night now it was a different driver. Invariably they seemed afraid to be here. It struck Phillip as impossible that he'd ever thought this was the best street in his city. Han put his hand on Phillip's shoulder, as if to say goodbye. "I forgot."

Phillip watched Han run in through the kitchen door, across what had been Phillip's parking space. A moment later he came running out with a chair in his hands.

"Here," Han said. "This is your chair."

Phillip shook his head. "You want me to take this?"

"You have the space," Han said. "Look. The van is empty."

"Han," Phillip said. "Thank you. But—"

"This is the same chair. The original." Han flipped it over. Its underside was scored with age marks. "I've repaired it myself all this time."

Phillip nodded. It was true that there had been Friday evenings when the leg had wobbled, and then, having made mention of it, he would return a week later to find the seat stable.

"This is the same chair?"

"Both chairs are the same from forty years ago."

"Both?"

Han shrugged. "What can I say? I knew you'd have noticed if they changed."

The driver coughed into his fist. It was time to go.

Phillip looked to Han. "In that case, could you bring me my wife's chair instead?"

SEAN O'BRIEN

The Beautiful Librarians

(after 40+ years)

The beautiful librarians are dead,
The fairly recent graduates who sat
Like Françoise Hardy's shampooed sisters
With cardigans across their shoulders
On quiet evenings at the issue desk,
Stamping books and never looking up
At where I stood in adoration.

There were nine, there must have been,
Though it was novels that they read,
Not Hughes and Lowell, Larkin, Plath
And Yeats and Eliot and Auden,
New Lines and *The New Poetry*,
But Thomas Hardy, Margaret Drabble,
Doris Lessing, Woolf and Dreiser (?).

Once I glimpsed the staffroom
Where they smoked and (if the novels
Were correct) would speak of men.
I still see the blue Minis they would drive
Back to their flats around the park,
To Blossom Dearie and red wine
Left over from a party I would never

Be a member of. Their rooms looked down
On dimming avenues of lime.
I shared the geography but not the world
It seemed they were establishing
With such unfussy self-possession, nor
The novels they were writing secretly
That somehow turned to 'Mum's old stuff'.

Never to even brush in passing
Yet nonetheless keep faith with them,
The ice-queens in their realms of gold –
It passes time that passes anyway.
Book after book I kept my word
Elsewhere, long after they were gone
And all the brilliant stock was sold.

ANNA RAVERAT

Lost and Found

1. Lost: A tooth. I would lose more, of course, and this wasn't the first, but I remember the shock – I was stretching it with my tongue to see how far it would go and then enjoying the horror of the dangle – dangle stretch dangle stretch – and then it loosened entirely and was out. But another tooth soon filled the empty space.

2. Lost: A plastic horse called Treacle (my father suggested I name him Copenhagen, after the Duke of Wellington's horse) whose long flowing mane I thoroughly enjoyed trimming down to a stubby hedge. I suspected my mother of throwing him away in a fit of housekeeping but she never admitted it.

3. Found: Grown-ups can make quite a smell in the bathroom.

4. Lost: A pale denim jacket, with a zip up the front on the diagonal, the coolest item of clothing I had ever owned, last seen at the school disco on a seat at the side of the gym. Whoever took it had the sense never to be seen wearing it, but what was the point of stealing it then? I decided that they must have posted it to a cousin in Liverpool or Newcastle or Hull.

5. Lost: Hope. Of ever being able to turn cartwheels. A long line of cartwheels, one after the other, ending with a triumphant flourish of the arms. Even now, aged forty, I'll see an expanse of sand or grass and be filled with the same yearning.

6. Found: Agates on a beach on holiday in California. Real treasure in real life.

7. Found: A way to get bigger helpings of ice cream from Bud's ice-cream parlour in San Francisco. Bud liked the English accent and if you coupled it with extreme politeness and a toothy grin you could win an extra-big scoop of mint choc chip.

8. Lost: Physical intactness – clambering up some sheets of corrugated iron in our yard, I slipped and broke my left arm. I don't remember the pain, only the outrage: I was breakable! I had broken! But I mended. Recently I met an old guy who told me how he'd lost a leg and he made it sound easy.

9. Found: Mushrooms, a whole field of smooth white dots. This was a field I knew well but I had never seen it covered in mushrooms. I was vegetating in front of our small black and white TV when there was a knock at the door. It was the girl from the farm three fields away, her name was Julie and she wanted to go mushrooming. She had two baskets. I grumbled but my mother made me. We filled the baskets easily and went back with carrier bags, which we stuffed, and sold to teachers the next day for ten pence a bag. We never saw a mushroom in that field ever again.

10. Found: A tractor on the riverbed, red but rusting. Julie banged her leg on it while we were swimming one summer. It wasn't crashed and it was standing on all four wheels as it would have done in a farmyard so it looked like it had been put there deliberately and maybe it had.

11. Found: Make-up and hairspray, thanks to Julie, who was a helpful two years older than me and therefore expert in things I needed to know about if I was going to try and be hip.

12. Found: Boys! My first kiss was on a school trip to the Isle of Arran. There was another school staying in the same hostel and after days of alternate ignoring and teasing, at the end of the week, some of their boys snuck into the girls' dormitory and one of them was tall and slim with curly dark hair (I ignored his spots).

13. Lost: My unblinking loyalty to mint choc chip ice cream.

14. Found: A vibrator wrapped up in a sock in Julie's mum's sock drawer. I had never heard of such a thing and didn't have a name for it but I knew instantly what it was, because of the shape, and because Julie was giggling when she showed me, and especially because it was hidden.

15. Lost: A freckly classmate with sticky-outy hair called Stephen who was killed riding a motorcycle at the age of fourteen.

16. Found: The jangling keys to my own personal chamber of worry and doom, which I'd gladly lose.

17. Found: Kittens on someone else's farm. They said their dad would drown them so I took one home. Dad wanted to call her Bastet after the Egyptian cat-goddess but we went for Lily. She turned out to be the most annoying mammal in Yorkshire, which I was convinced was because of the trauma of being taken too soon from her mother, but knowing this was no help because Lily's only aim in life was to stand outside the kitchen window and HOWL, no matter what you fed her. I tried to soothe her, I tried to warn her that my parents' breakfasts could not be disturbed in this way but she paid no heed and one day my dad drove off with Lily, now known as Bastard, and dumped her somewhere a very long way away.

18. Lost: Mr Gill who owned the shoe shop. He hung himself, which I hadn't known was an option.

19. Lost: My virginity. I was almost sixteen so it was almost legal, and he was twenty-one. I had been in love with him since I was twelve.

20. Found: The novelty of pavements – the thing I liked most about going to university in a town was being able to walk out of the front door in pretty shoes, as opposed to great big muddy boots.

21. Lost: A gold locket, stolen from my room at college. It was my own fault for leaving the room unlocked. My grandmother gave it to me and inside was a curl of pale brown hair, which I've always assumed was hers but why would she wear a cut of her own hair? It must have been someone else's.

22. Found: Romance with a Russian sailor. He sailed into port on an enormous square-rigger with three masts and a crew of one hundred. That night I met him at a party on a Chinese junk in the same harbour, he was wearing a jaunty uniform and a round white sailor's cap and had blond hair. We only kissed once but he wrote to me twice and sent me a badge. I can't remember his name but it might have been Sergey.

23. Lost: Wellington, our dog, shot by a neighbour while my parents were out. He was old by then, blind with cataracts and developed the fatal habit of sleeping in the neighbour's garage. One hot day, the neighbour drove over him by mistake but this didn't quite kill poor Wellington so the neighbour carried him to a field, finished him off with a shotgun, buried him and left my parents a note on the kitchen table.

24. Found: A child, sobbing in the dairy aisle, by the milk. It took me ages to find the mother and I was desperate to get back to the boyfriend I'd left tucked up in bed.

25. Lost and found: A silver earring, one of a pair I was given for my tenth birthday. I noticed it was missing in the middle of a day when I was near Paddington station and I retraced my steps slowly, which made me look mad but only because of the difference in pace compared to everyone else. When I went to bed that night there it was, on my pillow.

26. Found: A pair of black cashmere gloves, one winter, on a train. I was cold and loveless but at least now not gloveless.

27. Found: When all is lost, and I am utterly convinced that worse things don't happen at sea, in these do or die moments, it's usually better just to do.

28. Found: It is not necessary to be in love with your lovers.

29. Found: My place in the pecking order of cooks (quite low, except for soups). Most people in my social circle were married by now, including me, but I couldn't clad a fish in salt or rustle up blueberry muffins. When did they all go to cooking school?

30. Lost: Buttons. Some drop off silently and you only miss them later. Some ping onto the table or floor and you pick them up, carefully stow them in pocket or purse, meaning to sew them on again later, but other events come up, more urgent than the little button, which is anyway safe in your pocket or purse, but somehow, eventually, disappears.

31. Lost: A friend. (Not Julie – she'd gone already, to Manchester, married a dentist.) We met at college, she was bright and adventurous, funny, prone to bouts of low confidence, made great curry, danced well. We were friends for twenty years, took our babies to paddling pools and playgroups, but the friendship didn't stretch enough to span our difficulties and it snapped. Perhaps we were more alike than either of us knew.

32. 'Lost': A plastic car my daughter had loved. It took up so much room and was so noisy and ugly and anyway she was growing out of it. I threw it out in a fit of housekeeping and never admitted it.

33. Lost: Days upon days. I don't mean gone, because all the

days so far are gone, but some have been well lived in and others have been lost.

34. Found: Disappointments, squirreled away. I can be hanging out a wash, picking up toys, making (excellent) soup, and unwittingly dislodge one and it falls like a nut onto my head. I should pay attention to them but mostly I sweep them under a carpet, which is bad housekeeping. The other day I stumbled on a big pile of them and their attendant grief.

35. Found: Fear of filing. I cannot be the only one oppressed for years at a time by piles of unopened bank statements, boxes of photographs, empty photograph albums, stacks of phone bills the tax man might one day want to see (but why?), envelopes that should be reused (but when?).

36. Found: A small white downy feather floating down from the sky.

37. Found: Wrinkles: tiny, precise, determined like a baby's fist.

38. Found: A ten-pound note, on the busy high street on a sunny Saturday afternoon. My daughter saw it too, but I reached it first. Since it was a windfall, and, more especially since she was crying because thoughtless mummy had snatched up the banknote from under her five-year-old nose,

we thought the best thing to do was spend it on ice creams; vanilla for me, and for her a double scoop of mint choc chip.

39. Found: A pair of round, brown sunglasses with tortoise-shell frames and gold insignia on the sides. They cost a week's salary. They were never out of my sight, so to speak, but somehow they disappeared. I searched for them every summer. Then fashion favoured smaller, narrower, darker eyewear, so I bought some of those but they didn't suit me. Ten years later big sunnies were in again and the old ones turned up, in a drawer, under a pair of stockings. Clever sunglasses, they had just been waiting for the right time. Also, they cover up some of the wrinkles and I think (hope) that maybe I might still look OK in them?

40. It's hard to be hip at forty.

'Hello, kettle'

Where's Shirley? wonders George, looking round the kitchen. His wife appears to be out and he's thirsty, needs a cup of tea. He frowns, disconcerted. Normally she makes it for him and he isn't sure he can remember how.

'Hello, kettle,' he says, unplugging it. 'How are you this morning?'

He shuffles over to the sink, pyjama bottoms brushing the floor, listens as water fills the chrome drum; it echoes, like a bell. He lifts it, judges the weight, turns off the tap, shuffles back. Where *is* Shirley? Hmm . . . What was he doing? Oh yes. Making tea. He peers at the kettle. Plug in, switch on, red light; that's it.

He gets two bags out of the jar, puts them on the sideboard. 'Hello, teabags.'

They stand up like little pyramids, no, not pyramids – tents. Homes for ants. Or jaunty hats for tiny people. Yes, that's what they are; people in hats.

'Hello, kettle'

'Mrs PG,' he says, patting one. 'Mr PG,' he puts another, a few inches away, picks out a third, from an adjacent jar. This one is square, with a string and a tag. He examines the label: *Earl Grey.* An aristocrat, then.

He picks up Mrs PG, jumps her up and down. 'Hello, Mr PG.' His voice is high-pitched.

'Hello, Mrs PG,' he replies, timbre deeper. 'How are you today?'

'I'm fine. How's the Earl?'

He jiggles the square teabag. 'Very well, thank you.' The Earl is distinctly plummy.

George scratches his head. Where *is* his wife? His attention shifts; now the water's boiled. 'Time to go,' he tells Mrs PG. All at once, he feels sad. He doesn't want to cover her in boiling water; murder her, like a lobster. He puts her back in the jar, along with Mr PG.

'Sorry, old boy,' he says to the Earl, and before he can feel sympathy for him, picks up the square teabag and drops it into a mug.

As he finishes pouring, the phone rings. He lifts the receiver, but the wire is coiling in on itself, tangles of grubby white plastic. He holds the cable to shoulder height and drops the receiver so gravity can untwist it.

'Hello . . . hello . . .' He can hear a dim voice on the other end, down by the floor.

Eventually the wire stops twirling. Job done, he reaches for the receiver and puts it to his ear. 'Hello.'

'Dad?'

George doesn't recognize many people on the phone these days, even voices he can tell from the way they speak to him that he should. It makes him feel guilty, stupid – and he's not stupid. Luckily he knows this person. 'Yes. It is I, your father.' His is still playing at being posh, like the Earl. 'Hello, dear, how very nice to hear from you.'

'Are you OK?'

'Yes.' He is indignant. Why wouldn't he be?

'What are you doing?'

He looks about him. 'Er, I'm not sure.'

'It's just you picked up the phone, and then you didn't say anything.'

'Did I? I'm sorry, Karen. But I'm fine.' He pauses, considering. His ankle hurts and his stomach aches. 'Well, fine as can be expected. I'm getting old. I'm seventy-nine, you know.'

'I do know, yes, though actually—'

'I'm not dead yet, if that's why you were asking.'

Karen laughs. 'Of course that's not what I meant. Anyway, as long as you're all right. I was just calling to let you know we'll be back home soon.'

'Really? You're coming here? How lovely. I don't know where your mum is, though . . .'

'Mum's with me, Dad. We've been to the supermarket. You weren't up when we left, and we thought you deserved a lie-in. But we needed to go shopping, so we left you a note on the kitchen table.'

George looks at the table. It's red Formica, very familiar. It appears to be covered in small bits of something white.

'Hold on a minute.' He puts the phone down, goes over to the table, examines it. There are lots of screwed-up pieces of paper, tiny little balls. Who put them there? He returns to the phone. 'No note.'

'Oh well, never mind. We'll be back soon, all of us.'

'All of you?'

'Yes, Dad, we've come to stay for the weekend, Simon and me and the children.'

'Oh . . . yes . . .' Through the fog of George's memory, something almost comes into focus. Then, like a car on the motorway, *whoosh*, it's gone. He can't keep up. 'Simon . . .' He searches for the connection. *Whoosh*, he's got it. 'Karen–Simon–Molly–Luke!' Listing his daughter's family is the only way he can remember what his grandchildren are called. Whereas Simon he knows; Simon has been with Karen for many years, they married before George's mind got so tangled up, like the phone wire.

*

'How was he?' asks Shirley. She's driving, eyes focused on the road.

'OK,' says Karen, slipping her mobile back in her handbag. Dad's Alzheimer's is getting worse, she thinks, but her mum has enough to manage with her father's illness and having them all to stay; Karen spares her the observation.

'He seems to have missed the note though, and I'm not sure he's remembered what day it is.'

'At least he hasn't burnt the house down.' Shirley laughs, but Karen knows it's a genuine fear.

God knows how he'd manage without Mum to act as a safety net, thinks Karen. We should do more. But it's hard when we live so many miles away and with two small children. At least we've made the effort to be with him today, she reminds herself. Her friends were keen for her to spend this weekend with them and in many ways she'd have preferred to.

*

Slowly, painfully, George rises from his chair at the kitchen table. His feet are not so good these days, he broke his ankle or something – he can't recall exactly what – a few years ago, and he's not been able to walk well since. He's supposed to exercise, but it hurts to do so.

Meanwhile, the doorbell. Why doesn't Shirley answer it? She normally beats him to it, so when they have visitors, George only has to stand up, try to be courteous. Sometimes he finds that hard, especially with those he doesn't know. Which is an awful lot of people these days.

The bell rings again.

'All right, ALL RIGHT!' He shuffles down the hall, props himself on various resting places, breathing heavily; the cellar door handle, the banisters, the narrow table where Shirley puts the post.

He can see two figures through the glass: one tall, thick-set; the other smaller, with a curtain of chestnut hair.

'Hi, George,' says the tall one, when George opens the door. A small boy darts under his arm and down the hall. 'Luke, mind your grandfather! Sorry to make you get up – we haven't got keys. Shirley's putting the car in the garage.'

George recognizes Simon. He is laden with carrier bags. 'What have you got there?'

'Don't you remember, Dad? We've been to buy food for later,' says Karen. In her arms is a very small child dressed in a pink sunhat; she looks about a year old.

'I hope you didn't buy *that*.' George nods at the little girl and chuckles, pleased with his joke.

'Molly?' Karen lifts the sunhat to kiss her daughter's plump cheek. 'No . . . You weren't on sale in the supermarket, were you, Molster?'

George follows them – table, banister, handle – into the kitchen and sinks – 'Ooh, that's better' – into a chair. Before him are little pieces of paper; he has been unravelling them. He's recognized the writing on them as Shirley's, so he's been trying to reassemble them into something coherent.

'I think that's your mum's note,' says Simon, jerking his head.

'Oh, *Dad*,' says Karen.

George flushes. She's made him feel stupid, but he's not stupid, or never used to be. He can feel anger rising up through his core, like lava. Rage seems to come so quick, as if he's lost the lid to his emotions. 'Well, you bloody well put it together, then. FUCK YOU!' he bursts out, and sweeps the pieces of paper onto the floor. Ha! Now they'll have to pick them up. He's old, doesn't have to. He sits back in his chair, grins, a gargoyle content.

Molly starts to cry.

'Here, take her.' Karen hands Simon the little girl and sits down next to George. 'I'm sorry, Dad, I didn't mean to upset you.' She reaches to squeeze his knee. 'You OK?'

But the baby is wailing right by George's ear; the noise is awful. 'SHUT UP SHUT UP SHUT UP!' he yells, which only makes Molly cry harder.

'Best leave you to it,' Simon says, and he carries Molly from the room.

That's better: quiet. George feels the anger subsiding. 'I'm fine.' He pauses, considering. His ankle hurts and his stomach aches. 'Well, fine as can be expected. I'm seventy-nine, you know.'

'I do know, yes. Though actually, you're not—'

'I'm not dead yet.'

Karen sighs, then laughs; he senses her affection. 'No, Dad, I can see that.'

'And you?'

'Oh, I'm fine too,' says Karen.

'No, I meant how old are you now, dear?'

'Don't you remember . . . ?' She seems about to say more when his wife bustles into the kitchen with yet more bags of shopping.

*

'Where's your dad?' asks Simon, tipping a bag of crisps into a large salad bowl.

Karen is arranging a platter of sandwiches; she's put Molly in her high chair so she's free to help. 'In the living room with Luke, watching a cartoon.'

'Do you think he's any idea why we're all here?'

'He seems to have completely forgotten.'

'That's a shame.'

'I know. He could remember last year, and it wasn't such a big deal. Hey ho.' She laughs. 'I wouldn't mind forgetting it myself.'

Her mother sweeps in from the dining room. 'Those ready?' She takes the sandwiches from Karen before she can answer. 'I'll pop them on the table, and we're pretty much set.'

*

'Come on, George old boy,' says Simon. 'Time to turn this off.'

George is enjoying the cartoon. It's bright and colourful and the songs are really funny. 'Can't I just watch this?'

'You can come back to it later,' says Simon. 'Right now we need you next door.'

'I like it here,' says George. He's on the sofa next to his grandson – he can't remember his name, but they're both perfectly happy.

'Now come on, George, you've been watching telly for ages. There are lots of people here to see you. They've come specially.'

'I thought they weren't just here for Grandpa,' says the little boy.

George hasn't the faintest idea what they're on about, and the idea of lots of people makes him anxious. 'I'm staying here.'

But Simon turns off the TV.

'Hey! I was watching that!'

'You'll enjoy it once you're in there, I promise you.'

'Yes, come on, Grandpa,' says the boy. 'I'm hungry.'

'He still refusing to join us?' says Shirley from the doorway.

George looks at her. She is frowning, appears agitated. It makes him agitated too. 'Yes, I bloody well am!' he says.

'Grandpa's scaring me.' The little boy sitting next to him recoils.

'BLEURRGGHHH!' says George, and leans into him, pulling his gargoyle face. He just means to be funny, but the little boy jumps up and runs from the room. Now George feels guilty. 'OK, I'll come,' he says and slowly, creakily, gets to his feet. It's hard work. They clearly don't appreciate how much it pains him. 'Anything to stop all of you nagging.'

He edges out of the door – grasps the handle, then the banister for support – and manoeuvres himself round into the dining room.

Good Lord! The room is full of people. Lots and lots of them! When did they all arrive? Though maybe the doorbell has been ringing . . .

There are balloons hanging by the French windows, and on the table is an incredible array: neat triangular sandwiches with many different fillings, crisps and Twiglets, mini-sausages and Scotch eggs, chocolate biscuits and – his favourite – Garibaldis. What's all this for? he wonders, and pops a Garibaldi in his mouth.

Karen is sitting at the head of the table. She is attending to a small child in a high chair next to her, but stops what she's doing when she sees him. 'Dad!' She beams. 'Come up here, beside me.'

'Let me escort you to your place of honour,' says Simon, and the guests part so he can get through.

There's a chair on the other side of Karen's. He sits down and Simon hurries from the room.

Immediately the guests start coming forward, patting him on the back, saying, 'Congratulations, George!' and kissing Karen, too. He's confused, giddy from all the attention and the effort of trying to work out who's who.

Someone cries, 'Ready?' and the lights go out, the dining-room door is flung wide. He sees the glow first, then his wife comes into the room bearing a huge cake, her face lit up by candles. Behind her is Simon, with a second cake, his face also bathed in light. The crowd parts again as the two of them make their way to the head of the table. Shirley puts one cake down before him; Simon puts the other in front of Karen. There are dozens of candles, too many to count.

Suddenly, like a dolphin emerging from the sea, the

memory surfaces and arches up, free and glorious: he and his daughter were born on the same day, exactly four decades apart. George roars with delight.

'It's our birthday!' he says, and claps his hands.

GRAHAM ROBB

The Forty Immortals

The word *petruconti* has never appeared in print. It may never have existed. If it did exist, it would have been the Gaulish word for 'forty'. In the language of the ancient Gauls, '*petru*' meant 'four' and '*conti*' was the decimal multiplier, as in '*triconti*' ('thirty'). But until someone finds the word etched on a pot, scratched on a curse-tablet or quoted in an ancient text, it has to be preceded by an asterisk. This is the etymologist's sign for an unattested, made-up word. The asterisk serves as a warning: *petruconti* is just a plausible phantom, a possible imposter at the feast of language.

Gaulish belongs to a group of extinct languages known as Continental Celtic. For more than a thousand years, it was spoken by Druids and warriors, farmers and hill-fort dwellers from the Atlantic Ocean to the Alps. Some time after AD 400, it disappeared. A fourth-century historian mentions a Druid prophetess predicting the downfall of a

Roman emperor 'in the Gallic tongue'. The last unambiguous reference to Gaulish appears in a letter written by Sidonius Apollinaris in AD 474. He celebrates the fact that the aristocrats of the Arverni tribe have finally 'resolved to forsake the barbarous Celtic dialect'.

Even if records have been kept, it is hard to say exactly when a language dies. The last person to speak Gaulish probably lived in the Auvergne, where Gaulish place names are thicker on the ground than elsewhere, and where the plebs presumably continued to tell incomprehensible jokes in their barbarous dialect about those Latin-speaking Arvernian nobles. But after the last native speaker's final utterance – a prayer, a bequest, a term of endearment – the language would have lived on in the memory of the last listener, the last person who could curse, sing a baby to sleep or count up to forty in Gaulish. Eventually, the only Gaulish sounds to be heard in the French countryside were the strange quarter tones of wordless chants with which cowherds lulled their cattle.

Now, the language is a tattered cloak dug out of a peat bog. Only one of the four seasons is known – 'spring' ('*uisonna*'). We can say 'intelligence' ('*menman*') but not 'stupidity', 'beer' ('*curmi*') but not 'wine', 'drunk' ('*mesco*') but not 'sober'. The names of all twelve months have survived, but no one has yet been able to work out which is which.

Modern French contains fewer than two hundred words of Gaulish origin. They include '*boue*' ('mud'), '*bouge*' ('hovel'), *'décombres'* ('ruins'), *'suie'* ('soot'), *'blaireau'* ('badger'), *'vouge'* ('pruning-knife') and *'landes'*, which is the name of the French département whose number is 40. Those words are lucky to have survived. Almost four centuries ago, a body of learned writers and orators was created to defend the French language. Their principal function is to compose a dictionary of the French language as it should be spoken and written. They call themselves the Forty Immortals, and their average age is seventy-eight.

No one knows why Cardinal Richelieu chose the number forty when he created the Académie Française. Perhaps he was thinking of the biblical number of days required for a rite of passage or a course of training (the Flood, the forty days in the wilderness, and so on). Forty has proved an elusive total. It took four years for the Académie Française to reach its full complement, which it maintained for fourteen months, until 1640, when one of the original immortals died. The life expectancy of an Immortal is well below the national average. 'There has never been a better time to apply to the French Academy', a French publisher told me recently, alluding to the fact that four seats were vacant. She liked the idea of an *'Anglais'* sitting in the Academy. Ever since the Immortals devised the grammatical rules with which pedants torment their pupils, no native has been able to speak French correctly. Only a foreigner who has learnt the language rule by rule can claim to be faultless. The polite expression, 'You speak perfect French,' does not mean, 'You speak French like a native.' My French translator, whose

French actually *is* impeccable (she was educated in Casablanca), sent me a photograph of her desk on which a book stands ready at all times: *Pièges et difficultés de la langue française* ('Traps and Pitfalls of French').

With the Immortals in control, the feast of language turned into a private dinner party. Admission to the *Dictionnaire de l'Académie Française* is not automatic, as the Academy's website explains: 'Words, definitions and new meanings, when they arouse discussion [in other words, when enough academicians are in attendance and awake], are accepted or rejected by vote, as though they were laws or people.' As in most other domains of French public life, connections are vital. A word that wanders in off the street is unlikely to be given a seat at the table: 'The *Dictionnaire* does not contain quotations and hardly ever refers to authors by name. This is partly a matter of tradition, but also of discretion: were there to be quotations, they would, of necessity, be taken, for the most part, from members of the Company who are either present or who have disappeared' (that is, permanently disappeared). The paradoxical implication is that correct language is the language used by the people who compile its dictionary.

For a word to be accepted, it must spend a certain period in quarantine. (The word is related to '*quarante*' and refers to the ritual forty days of purification.) 'One must wait in order to recognize the words that are truly necessary.' If it proves a useful, healthy sort of word, it will eventually be admitted to the dictionary. But many words die in quarantine: by the time they become acceptable and the dictionary has reached their initial letter, they may no longer be in use.

Given the Academy's linguistic xenophobia, it is surprising that a few English words have gained admittance. But like the mentally retarded natives of French colonies who were presented in Paris *salons* as typical specimens of their race, many of these English words serve to underline the inferiority of 'Anglo-Saxon' civilization: '*baby-foot*', '*blue-jean*', '*cafétéria*', '*chewing-gum*', '*chips*' ('could be replaced by "*croustilles*"'), '*ketchup*' ('probably from the Chinese'), etc.

Non-immortals have been trying to gate-crash the dinner party almost since the beginning. Honoré de Balzac wrote a series of Rabelaisian tales in mock-Old French to show how many deliciously disgusting words of Gaulish origin had been expunged from the language. (Three series of ten tales were published; a fourth, comprising numbers thirty-one to forty, was planned but never completed.) One of the great dictionaries and reference works of the nineteenth century was deliberately anti-Academic. Pierre Larousse, the son of a blacksmith, began work on his *Grand Dictionnaire universel* in 1840. After publishing forty bestselling textbooks, he was able to pay his contributors more generously than most publishers of the time. One of his contributors, Jules Andrieu, found that he could live on four thousand lines a month. On the eve of publication in 1863, Larousse, who was by then in his mid-forties, calculated that the manuscript, divided into two piles, would form a full-scale model of the towers of Notre-Dame, which means that the whole manuscript must have been over four hundred feet high. Instead of borrowing his dictionary definitions from all those 'dreary and insipid authors' approved of by the French Academy, he gave deliberately unruly examples:

Quarante

'Forty gentlemen dined on the floor below, and each one drank the health of forty people.' (Mme de Sévigné)

'Maximin ate forty pounds of meat in a single day.' (Chateaubriand)

'At sixteen, a girl turns up her nose at the most handsome and virtuous of lovers; at forty, she takes whatever's on offer.' (Boursault)

Now, in the fourth century of their existence, the Forty Immortals, like a band of aged suicide bombers, are bent on extinction. If *'businessmen'* (*'hommes d'affaires'* is the correct term) follow the Academy's advice, they will be rendered practically speechless and forced to converse exclusively in English. Academicians themselves usually restrict their vocabulary when speaking in public, for fear of error, and compensate by using extraordinarily contorted syntax more reminiscent of German. Like Marie-Antoinette fleeing from the Revolution through the excremental alleyways of Paris, the Perpetual Secretary, Mme Hélène Carrère d'Encausse, litters her articles and speeches with phrases such as 'that horrible expression . . .' or 'that awful word . . .'. Recently, she warned that French is not only 'besieged' by German and 'invaded' by English, it is also under attack from French regional languages, which are 'of foreign origin'. 'National identity' (widely used as a racist euphemism) will be 'shattered' if 'the French language, which is the sole incarnation and custodian of our moral and cultural unity, is condemned to share this role with the languages of France, which are legion.' Her fellow Immortal, Bertrand Poirot-Delpech, backed her up in an article in *Le Monde* by heaping scorn on all those French 'dialects devoid of grammar'.

Among those bizarrely grammar-less languages, Gaulish probably has the best claim to being 'native'. But its contribution to French is negligible. Approximately one hundred and sixty-eight words are derived from Gaulish, but only eighty are found in standard, non-dialectical French. One day, if the Immortals are struck by a sudden epidemic, a *coup d'état* might bring in the rabble and fatten up the emaciated *Dictionnaire*. Or perhaps at last the Academy will be reduced to a single curmudgeon who refuses to elect anyone else and, as his parting shot at the sullied national language, produces a perfect dictionary consisting of blank pages.

Most French people couldn't care less, or, as they used to say, '*je m'en moque comme de l'an quarante*': 'I care about that as much as I do about the year forty.' The origin of the expression is obscure. Some lexicographers believe that this is a reference to the year 1040, when the world was supposed to end. Others see it as an aristocratic sneer at the Revolutionary calendar, which replaced the Christian calendar: year 40 of the French Republic was the distant day that would never dawn. But the most likely explanation is that '*l'an quarante*' is a corruption of '*l'Alcoran*': 'It means as much to me as the Koran.'

This might raise a smile when '*quarante*' is discussed in the patriotic Academy. Unfortunately, the fewer-than-Forty Immortals have yet to pronounce on the word. The latest fascicle of the dictionary ended at '*quadrivium*' (the four subjects taught in medieval universities). '*Quarante*' is still in quarantine and will probably not be out until October 2012.

ROBIN ROBERTSON

Argentiera

Under the ruins of the old silver-mine
the sea is wild. Children go in
off these rocks all summer

and the waves, like their lives, raise them up
and let them down,
haul them up and drop them –

except for one swimmer, and the one great wave
that won't stop falling: that takes his legs
and then just holds him under.

JON RONSON

---

40 Things To Do Before I Die:
A Bucket List

1. Reach that moment when ambition dies and I just feel unaccountably happy with what I've got. This does happen. According to my mother. She said to me, "You know how every day for you is like a scream of panic and anxiety and the need to always be achieving. Well, you may not realize it, but that fades. Ambition fades."

2. If it does fade I can take up gardening or something, I don't know.

3. Or yoga. Although the only time I've ever done yoga – my wife forced me into it – I got a trapped nerve and I was in so much pain by the time we got home we had to call the ambulance. It was chaos. I was in spasms. My son was yelling at my mother, "YOU CAUSED THIS!" The ambulance man evidently felt I was overreacting. He said,

"Different people react to pain in different ways." Then he shot me a quite withering look and told me I didn't need to go to hospital. So not yoga.

4. I'm already a keen walker, so maybe I'll just walk for longer distances. Although I can't just keep walking for years until I die once my ambition fades. I'll get exhausted. Imagine the damage to the knees. I'll need to intersperse it with something else.

5. But what? God. I don't know. Sitting? Gazing out?

6. Maybe I'll become an inventor. I've already invented those Heely shoes that turn into roller-skates when you walk on them in a certain way. I invented them in my mind before I knew they already existed.

7. I rather like the idea of being a sort-of kindly, eccentric inventor, like Caractacus Potts. Children will delight in my kooky ways.

8. Stop going to parties. I just don't enjoy them. What's the point? You have to talk loudly to strangers about nonsense. Where's the benefit? As the night wears on I see others grow increasingly effervescent whereas I feel a crushing need to go home and be alone.

9. I'm thinking that this crushing need to go home after an hour or two out of the house probably means that, in practice, children won't delight in my kooky ways when I become an inventor. Basically I'll be able to be delightful for

a short time, then a look of tiredness and self-doubt will cross my face, and I'll have to excuse myself. This unexpected mood-shift will confuse and disappoint children.

10. Now I've read Susan Cain's book on introverts, *Quiet*, I realize all this isn't just me. It's a trait shared by introverts the world over. We feel this way because our brains are especially sensitive to overstimulation. So: that aspect of my personality I had found shameful is actually an indicator that I'm amazing. I never have to go to another party again.

11. In fact all that's stopping me from turning down every party invitation right now are my wife and son. "But we *have* to go to this party," they say. Well I'm going to start saying, "*You* go. I'm staying home."

12. What am I doing, sentencing myself to twilight years of insular misery? There has to be a better way than this.

13. Stay in one of those Polynesian hotels on stilts where tropical fish swim underneath. I can wake up in the morning and climb out of bed and dive into the crystal waters.

14. I'll swim out as far as the eye can see. "Come!" I'll yell to my wife and son. And they'll dive in after me. And we'll swim and swim, throwing our heads back and laughing.

15. But later, if they want me to have a kind of traditional Polynesian massage I'll say . . .

16. "No thank you. I just don't enjoy massages. I find them too intimate."

17. Take heroin. Maybe when I'm about seventy. When there's nothing to do for the rest of the day and there's enough money in the bank that I can just buy more without having to commit crimes if it proves to be too moreish.

18. I reckon the heroin will definitely help with point 16. Although not with points 13 or 14. And definitely not with point 7.

19. Start smoking again. When I'm on heroin.

20. Go back to Cardiff. A young child will come up to me and say, "What are you thinking about, mister?" I'll bend down and tell them a moving story with a powerful message about following their dreams. Their eyes will light up. And I'll just walk away into the fog, nobody knowing who that old man was or what he did.

21. While I'm in Cardiff I'll track down and apologize to a boy I used to know called Richard. We were best friends in Cardiff High School for a while. Years ago I wrote a column for the *Guardian* in which I mused upon why the most popular kids in school didn't do so well in their subsequent lives, whereas the bullied nerds tended to soar. I cited Richard as an example of the popular kid who failed to excel. I named him. What was I thinking? Why would I do that? These memories of shameful things I have done follow me around like dogs. So I have to either find him and apologize to him or just wait until I'm old enough for the memory of the whole incident to fade.

22. Speaking of memory loss, I'd like to know why we forget the good stuff but remember the bad stuff. Whatever happened to repressing bad memories? That doesn't seem to happen to me at all! My bad memories jump out at me in the dark like intruders. Whereas, say, the nice, simple romantic summer days with old girlfriends are just flashes of blurry colours now, just flashes of nothingness.

23. Like that field where my first girlfriend Anita and I walked that time. I'd like to find that field. But I haven't got a hope. I'm not even sure it's in Britain, and I can't ask Anita because she died.

24. This morning I was filling out a US immigration form and I had to look on Wikipedia to see how old I am.

25. Write *Quiet*, by Susan Cain. It is driving me nuts that she wrote this wonderful book and not me. So to achieve this I'd need to . . .

26. Invent time travel. Go back in time, grab her manuscript and . . .

27. I guess lock her in a dungeon or something. You know what? I don't like where this is going. Forget I said that.

28. Donate a lot of money to a charity. Yes. That's what I'll do.

29. By the way, while I'm back in time I'll decide not to make that Channel 4 documentary about the Alpha Course. This was a documentary about a course that tries to con-

vince agnostics to become Christians. The film was commissioned at a time when I'd suddenly decided to be incredibly nice about everyone in my documentaries. Anything that portrayed my interviewees as flaky or eccentric or crazy I'd leave out and only include the stuff that made them seem lovely and ordinary. And you know what? Nobody liked that documentary. The viewers didn't like it. Channel 4 didn't like it. I didn't like it. Even the interviewees essentially thought, "Meh." Channel 4 has never commissioned another documentary from me since. They've gone down the 'mocking gypsies' road and my Alpha film was as far from mocking gypsies as documentaries get. So I won't bother to make that film, now I'm back in time.

30. Also now I'm back in time I'll do something about the fact that I *knew* Google would be massive. I knew it before almost anyone did. Everyone else was making do with Dogpile and Alta Vista but I was on Google like a shot. I was an early adopter. So I'll do something about it! I don't know what I'll do. But I'll do something.

31. Also, now I'm back in time, I'll take the opportunity to tell myself, "Jon, you needn't worry every time you try and call home and they don't answer. It will turn out that they're *never dead*. They're always just at the shops or in a different room or they can't hear the phone or they just haven't bothered picking it up. All that worry – every second of that prickling anxiety – is pointless. You could have been having fun."

32. Stop feeling embarrassed. The other day the human-rights lawyer Clive Stafford Smith said to me, "Imagine how much better the world would be if we all had our perversions and our communicable diseases tattooed on our foreheads. Then nobody would be able to use them as weapons against us."

33. Take crack.

34. Climb Mount Everest.

35. Visit the Taj Mahal.

36. Have a threesome.

37. I don't feel anywhere near as embarrassed as I used to. It's as if my amygdala – the part of the brain that shoots the feelings of fear and guilt and remorse up and down to my central nervous system – has been deadened by chronic overuse.

38. I find myself unexpectedly admiring Max Mosley. There he was, president of Formula One, finally shaking the stigma of having two of the world's most infamous fascists as parents. Then he woke up one morning to discover a photograph of himself on the front page of the *News of the World* being whipped, naked, at an S&M brothel. I bet the newspaper was gambling on him being so frozen with embarrassment he wouldn't dare to poke his head up to fight the untruth that it was a "Nazi orgy". But instead he seemed to realize that embarrassment was only a feeling –

a kind of pact between the humiliator and the victim. As soon as the victim stepped out of the pact by refusing to feel ashamed, the whole thing crumbled.

39. Speaking of clever people utilizing embarrassment in an attempt to make others compliant: a few years before the housing market crashed I asked a subprime lender why his clients rarely defaulted on their loans. They were diligently paying the interest on their interest-only mortgages, allowing themselves to be indentured servants for life, so what was stopping them from just stopping? He said, "Embarrassment." He was gambling, wrongly as it transpired, that their fear of embarrassment would keep them from transgressing.

40. You know what? Feeling no embarrassment, stopping going to parties, and hopefully one day forgetting the bad things I've done are surely the three greatest advantages of growing old.

ALICE SEBOLD

Childless

They start when you're young: Barren, frigid, sterile. Later it is "selfish" that takes over, more popular by 1985, when you are twenty-two, to make it a flaw of character with a psycho-pop word. So you take it on: "Yeah, that must be it! I'm selfish!" or, if there is no sense of irony in the room, you turn serious. "Actually, maybe I will someday but I'm in my twenties and I live in New York." Translation: Let me have this time, please, this paltry decade of adulthood.

One day, you are present at work when they vote against hiring another woman. "She'll just pop one out and take paid leave." You are present for so long without popping one out yourself that you frequently overhear the word "dyke" as you pass in the hall. When you cut your hair short, you're asked flat out by a man in accounts. Big mistake then. You sue for sexual harassment. What are you? A lightweight, a whiner, a malcontent? You withdraw the suit and begin to grow your hair (truth is a pixie cut is meant for very few). Six months later, you're fired. This is a relief, but overnight Manhattan has become a maternity ward. Every friend is stopping, popping, and then rolling on four wheels out to Long Island or up the Hudson. Warming buns are spread out up in the Adirondacks, down in Florida, across the ocean in London.

At thirty-six, standing up for your choice results in a young man asking you, "Alice, why do you hate children so much?" Cornered, you know it's best not to say, "Are you a child, because I'm hating you right now." Instead, with a table of faces turned to hear your answer you grow calm: "Just because I don't intend to have any doesn't mean I hate them. Actually, I pity them." "I pity you," says the young man.

In your late thirties, there is an increasing discussion of clocks. In an interview, a Swiss journalist says, "Tick-tock, you're not getting any younger." "So being a writer isn't enough? I also have to be a mother?" "You are not really a woman otherwise, no?" I never adjust to this nasty, baiting style of questioning. In Berlin, a journalist (and a dyke for godssakes!) tells me she would have become a novelist and flown around the world, too, if she hadn't had a child. "A child is more important than a book," she says. I'm losing it. "Every child is more important than any book? Is that it? All of Proust? All of Tolstoy? Shall we throw in Shakespeare?"

Back home I move from New York to California. I

befriend a young woman who lives near me. She's heard about my work, that it has meant I'm in the pages of *Vogue*. "I'll show you mine if you show me yours." I am excited. What has she done? "Mine" is a review of a book I wrote. "Hers" is a snapshot of her wedding, which is printed in the letters section of *Martha Stewart Magazine*. I say nice things. I fawn, mimicking what I've seen others do. Later, I despair.

Foolishly, I believe I have four more years until I slip soundlessly over what I think of as the fatal hurdle and will no longer be bludgeoned by the *central and increasingly annoying question that women are expected to answer even when it has nothing to do with how they define themselves* . . .

But I am wrong!

At forty, a true frenzy begins, the "last copter out" mentality. It is so fervent, so right-wing in its nuanced propaganda. "Look, supermodels have them, celebrities have them, grandmothers in Italy and plastic surgery addicts in Santa Monica are doing it simultaneously and in multiples!" "Are you sure you don't want to? Sure? Why not? You can still, you know, and as a writer, you have plenty of free time . . . " (What? What an assumption! My life is pure hell! Pure artistic hell! No time. None at all. Nada, get me?) But you don't counter and you don't joke. The baby shit is serious and it is EVERYWHERE and you realize that from when you were twenty-two to when you were forty-two, which you are not anymore, the fatal hurdle moved in the middle of the night and is still moving, and friends your age – you're

OLD now! – are living with the questionable percentage-of-success rates as science presses endlessly onward into the womb.

You sit and you think, "Should I?" Say to your husband: "Should we?" and the questioning always leads to the same answer from both: "I don't want to, but do you?" "No, no, I don't." And I think it's over, Yes, I think it's done. Could I? Probably, say the Italian grandmothers. Probably not, say recent medical studies. As the days pass and I enter – finally – the age of only miraculous scientific possible pregnancy I realize what is slowly overwhelming me. It is an amazing, an *incredible* sense of relief. I don't hate them. As a matter of fact, I pity them. The weight on their heads can be so heavy, the hope they symbolize for the hopeless, that they may spend their whole miserable lives feeling unable to fulfill those who gave birth to them and the society that believes that they are the future. Let them be what they will. In the end, leave them be.

EMMA STRAUB

Gifts I Would Like to Receive for
My 40th Birthday

A year and a half ago, I turned thirty, a number I'd been dreading for some time. Thirty turned out to be wonderful— I felt free of the insecurities I'd been plagued by in my teens and twenties. Now that I'm a proper adult, with a husband and a mortgage and two cats and a car and so forth, time feels more precious to me. What did I do but worry with all those free hours in my youth? If the twenties were about anxiety, and the thirties are about reality, I see no reason why the forties shouldn't be pure, glorious fantasy. With that in mind, I have made a brief list of gifts I would like to receive for my fortieth birthday, which will occur in 2020, giving you plenty of time to acquire them for me.

1 A safari, preferably the kind where I would occasionally sleep in a hotel with giraffes nearby, friendly ones that

Gifts I Would Like to Receive for My 40th Birthday

   would poke their soft faces through the second-story windows to share my breakfast with me.

2 One glittering tiara for special occasions, such as dinner with royalty, politicians, and my parents. The central diamond should be no smaller than a baby's fist.

3 One more subdued tiara, to be worn to the grocery store and dry-cleaner and such. Central diamond should be no larger than a baby's fist.

4 A baguette machine, which will produce fresh baguettes at every meal, always crunchy on the outside and soft in the middle. This gift may require a full-time, live-in baker, which I would also begrudgingly accept.

5 An entire year of rent and room service at a five-star hotel, with unlimited rides on the elevator, suspenders, pleated skirts, and bows for my hair, as well as a pet turtle, who I could take for long walks up and down the carpeted hallways.

6 One butter sculpture, preferably in the shape of a horse.

7 One pair ruby slippers, complete with time-travel potential.

8 One full year of perfect autumn days. (Comes with appropriate sweaters, jackets, boots, and scarves.)

9 Simple (expert) proficiency in the following: surfing, speaking French, playing the ukulele, gardening, cheese-making, harmonizing, lindy-hopping.

10 A three-story library with a sliding ladder and all the books I've never read. This gift may require a full-time, live-in, extremely handsome librarian. So be it.

GRAHAM SWIFT

'Writers, writers!'

When I last contributed to a Picador birthday anthology, for Picador's twenty-first, the idea was that each writer would pick a year from the twenty-one of Picador's existence and say why it had been important to them. I chose 1974, when I turned twenty-five, because it was a watershed year for me. I turned forty in 1989 and, whatever turning forty meant for me privately, the year was certainly a watershed year for the world. In a series of extraordinary political upheavals, the Iron Curtain was lifted and the Berlin Wall came down. It felt like one of history's new dawns.

I can claim a certain personal synchronicity in all this, since I was born in 1949 and have always seen myself as a 'cold-war baby'. Now the cold war was suddenly melting. When the 'velvet revolution' was beginning in Czechoslovakia I was commissioned by *Granta* magazine to go to Prague to write about it—though my visit also had another particular aim. I was there during the December days when the communist regime fell and (though the weather stayed frozen) the cold war which had been a fact of my forty years of life gave up another of its strongholds. The piece I wrote is included, as is my 1974 piece, in *Making an Elephant*, an autobiographical selection of my non-fiction that Picador brought out in 2009.

The number forty has its meanings for me. I was born at the end of the Forties, one of the worst decades in history. Perhaps more mass killing, atrocity and misery were perpetrated in those ten years than in any other decade before or since. If I was a cold-war baby, I was also born into the shadow of the Second World War and into a sense of things that, when I grew up to be a writer, I'd feel in my bones: that our little personal histories (my starting and finishing point as a novelist) are inextricably linked with and coloured by 'big history'. Sometimes, indeed, big history completely consumes them, since that history is so often the history of war and oppression.

Looking again at that piece about my visit to Prague, during which I met more than one scarred Czech author, I notice that it employs a repeated exclamatory yet wry refrain: 'Writers, writers!' I think what I meant to convey was that whenever there are historic convulsions writers will always be there because such convulsions require writers to record them, but at the same time, even amid such convulsions and almost despite them, writers will always want to be writers. They are, in some people's eyes, an irrelevant, dispensable breed, but they are a hard breed to kill.

War of one kind or another rumbles through pretty well every novel I've written, either in the background or, as in my latest novel *Wish You Were Here*, as a disruptive claiming of the foreground. Now that I'm older myself than Picador's forty years, I can take a long, sober view of all this. Our capacity for conflict hasn't diminished in my lifetime, while the need for writers to acknowledge and explore this perennial tendency hasn't diminished since Thucydides.

Given the timing of my birth, it's not surprising that history has infiltrated my fiction. The Second World War seemed just over my shoulder, and by the time I was twenty-one and the world was mine, the world had known a good deal more bloodshed and grief. What is fairly surprising is that I have actually grown up to know—domestically, nationally—six decades of broad peace and even two genuine phases of euphoria. I mean the 1960s (though the cold war was then still very much escalating) and that moment at the end of the 1980s when the world changed. It proved to be a moment rather than a phase, since we all know how quickly the euphoria turned into something else. The 1990s, to think only of Europe, were not a benign decade so far as human conflict goes. And come the new millennium and a certain September day in 2001 the world would change again.

1989, when I was forty, was not a euphoric or peaceful year for writing, since it was the year in which the fatwa was issued against Salman Rushdie. I remember, that February, having for the first time the direct chilly feeling that writers really *were* people who could be seriously threatened for being what they were, for writing books. The timing was ironic, since my relatively mild trepidation was as nothing to what a host of writers had undergone during the grim decades of the cold war. Just ten months later I'd go to Prague specifically to track down one of those persecuted writers.

It's a further irony that another piece included in *Making an Elephant* is about the effect on me, at a much earlier time in my life, of reading the Russian writer Isaac Babel, one of several writers erased in their literary ascendancy by Stalin. In Prague I met those who drily said, 'You should have been here in Stalin's day.' Babel 'disappeared' before the term cold war was coined (not that its coinage made much difference to what went on inside Russia) and at the beginning of that dreadful decade of the 1940s. When he disappeared he would have been not much more than forty himself. Fortunately his writing, though long suppressed in Russia, could not be erased. Picador brought out a handsome edition of his complete work in 2002.

Lest what I'm writing seem a catalogue of gloom and the very opposite of a birthday celebration, let me restore some balance. The cliché that life begins at forty may have some validity for writers—if not for Babel. They seem often to go through a process of 'finding themselves' in their thirties and, after their first flush of actual youth, to discover a second literary youth which sees them fully fledged around forty. In 1989, aged forty, I felt neither wet behind the ears nor beyond my prime. I'd been a serious writer for a good twenty years, a published one (at least in book form) for only nine.

The preceding decade had been one of great excitement for me, as I think it was for many of my writer contemporaries. It was a decade in which, for whatever mixture of reasons, writing, new writing and particularly fiction, enjoyed a heyday—a sort of second, literary Sixties. Ironically, this occurred in the 'Thatcher years' of the Eighties, but the new writers then appearing had served their apprenticeships in the Seventies. One thing that gave them hope was that this was the time when Picador emerged and flourished and, with its distinctive style and declared aim to offer the best 'international writing', became really the publisher all writers yearned to be published by.

In 1982 there was a promotion called the Twenty Best Young British Novelists, for which it was shrewdly stipulated that young could mean up to forty. I'm struck by how many of that twenty are now, decades on, still going strong, still entirely in print and entirely alive. I'm struck, returning to 1989 and being forty, by how much in my own writing life was then still to come. It's good to know that forty can be, for writers at least, still infused with a feeling of freshness and setting forth—a sort of literary twenty-one.

Looking through my book of non-fiction, which straddles the forty years of Picador's life, I'm further struck by how much joy is recorded—in decades in which big history has offered few and fleeting causes for rejoicing. There has been the inherent joy in writing itself—certainly not an everyday joy, as every writer knows, or it would not be a joy, and a joy that has much pitted against it, but a joy, when it happens and grabs you, that makes it all worthwhile. And there have been the instances of joy I've found through other writers I've met and places I've been to, as secondary effects of being a writer.

Undoubtedly one of the best places ever for meeting other writers was the former Picador office in the Fulham Road—spilling over into the Park Walk restaurant round the corner—during the great days of the Seventies and Eighties. It truly was not so much an office as a rendezvous, a haunt—and, fortunately for me, a walkable distance from home. You might breeze in, with no particular purpose, and meet, because they'd just breezed in too, not just other novelists, but great reporters and travellers of the world: Michael Herr, Ryszard Kapuściński, Bruce Chatwin. You might find yourself drinking and lunching with them—lunches which at Park Walk often went on into the dusk—and even making a new friend.

It's chastening yet indirectly heartening to reflect that this heyday occurred in the 'free world' when, on the other side of a divide, writers were being regularly victimized and silenced. We shouldn't take lightly our freedoms, of writing and of publishing, or the fact that writers will always spring up, like shoots from the soil, and always want to be writers.

I began with a litany of woe and war and am ending with joy and friendship. The seeds of wanting to be a writer were sown in me early in life, but I've been an active, practising writer now for around forty years, the same length of years as Picador's. In all those years I've kept a two-fold faith that writing, which for me means principally fiction, can both look hard and honestly at what is difficult to look at in human history—'big' or 'little'—and, in its very creativity, its urge to bring things alive, its alertness and truthfulness to all the sensations, to the very taste of life, be fundamentally affirmative. As I put it in *Making an Elephant*, 'at most a celebration, at least a glow in the dark'.

It's in this twin spirit, but with a particular emphasis on the celebration, that I wish Picador a very happy fortieth birthday.

MIGUEL SYJUCO

The Forty

The discovery of the documents has been called, by some in certain circles, the find of the decade, if not the century. In the recent edition of *La Revue des mondes musulmans et de la Méditerranée*, Prof. Rachel Crawford, of Oxford University, reports that the pages were unearthed the first evening of this millennium by none other than Dr. Charles "Chucky" Kinbote, Jr., the controversial and reclusive orientalist from Eastern Europe. They were found, Dr. Kinbote claimed, in the College de France archives on 52 rue du Cardinal-Lemoine, among files once belonging to Louis Massignon. The manila envelope that contained them bore no stamps nor return address. Hastily opened by its original recipient, it is believed to have been delivered by hand to Massignon's office on Halloween, 1962, the very day a heart attack took the esteemed expert on Islamic Studies. It is unknown if Massignon knew of these palimpsests recounting the escape of the forty thieves from the manhunt led by Ali Baba.

The six sheets of uterine vellum originally bore intricate studies of the flora and fauna of Pepys Island, dated 1699, and were said to have been in good condition. However, a small stain of tincture of galls on the final page revealed Arabic calligraphy, as well as the red, vertical lettering of Mongol script—faded, like the memory of bloody knives. Dr. Kinbote has only provided photographic facsimiles of the text found beneath, and Prof. Crawford surmises, puckishly, that the sheets may have been manufactured by the William Cowley parchment works (which everyone in our field knows has been making vellum in Newport Pagnell, Buckinghamshire, since only 1870). Before angrily ceasing communication, Dr. Kinbote bristled at Prof. Crawford's implication that his manuscript will prove as authentic as Duncan Black MacDonald's Bodleian MS of the early 20th Century, or Maximilian Habicht's "Tunisian" Breslau edition of 1825.

In her article, Prof. Crawford does point out that Dr. Kinbote would be in good company, as neither Sir Richard Burton nor Antoine Galland himself ever proved the "orphan tales" of Ali Baba or Aladdin were part of the original *One Thousand and One Nights*. Galland, Prof. Crawford reminds us, first heard of Ali Baba on March 25, 1709, from the Maronite scholar Youhenna Diab, who had been brought from Aleppo to Paris by Paul Lucas, that famous traveller from Rouen.

The Forty

This reporter himself has travelled to Oxford for a brief interview with Prof. Rachel Crawford. She has revealed, for the first time, the full details of Dr. Charles Kinbote, Jr.'s, stunning account of the lives of the forty so-called thieves.

They hailed from all over, Crawford says Kinbote told her, chiefly from the corners of Khorasan (many from Sabzevar, Merv, and Herat, but more than a few from across Transoxiana and Khwarezmia). They were a motley crew, some from as far west as where the Atlas ranges met the endless ocean, with "the other three winds" represented by five Sogdian "brothers" from Samarkand, one Almohad cook from Al-Andalus, one Zagwean former slave captured by Saladin at the conquest of Al-Ludd, and a pair of eunuchs from the heights of Khotan who'd heard that in the Fergana valley striped horses who sweated blood would return them their manhood if tamed. From the east came a Khmer fisherman who searched in vain the Lancang, Yalong, and Indus rivers for any aquatic creature who could trump his mastery, and who sought the Nile upon hearing of the sacred twin fish Abtu and Anet, who swim along the ship that carries the sun god Ra. The farthest-flung pair of the forty arrived from Srivijaya and Mindanao, of where the best maps that existed at the time were written in their minds.

It is believed, Kinbote said, that his MS was prepared before 1387, by an unknown scholar, or scholars, who recorded the story from the female storyteller Mojgan of Esfahan, who was among the seventy thousand of that city massacred that year by Tamerlane. The tale begins with the speaker making a heartfelt plea for mercy. As she discusses all that she has seen in her life, her tone becomes defiant, as if killing her would deprive her captors of something truly unique. If you are not foolish and barbaric, Mojgan says at one point, my stories will become your stories. I will recount to you a tale, she says, of the Forty, the wisest of men who unwisely sought to right a wrong without sympathy and fell prey to their own avarice.

These Forty travelled widely, she says, on an assortment of fine horses and camels—not the finest, but those they'd come to know and love, for these men were sufficiently sage to be suspicious of perfection. The men carried not only scimitars and other arms, but also brass astrolabes, sewing and cooking implements, an "exquisitely crafted" equatorium, a djembe and an oud, telescopes, calligraphy brushes and paper, water skins, and an assortment of carpets. For trading, they had Yuan silks as well as amphorae of myrrh and argan oils. A library went with them always, limited only by how much their stoutest camel could carry. Their leader guarded carefully a copy of Al-Idrisi's world map, a "djellaba of shadows," and a splendid shatranj set with semi-precious figures for its wazirs, rukhs, al-fils, and asbs, ivory for its pawns, and an "emerald for one shah and a ruby for his fated foe."

This company of forty, Mojgan says, called themselves the "Badr" (بدر), roughly translated to "Men of the Full Moon," a possible reference to either the crescent of Islam, the passage of time, the study of astronomy, the illumination

of a dark night, or perhaps all of the above. These Badr followed the Platonic notion of male democracy, and they
believed in the Great Khan's support of free trade. They
idolized the seventh-century monk Xuan Zang's dedication
to travel, scholarship, and the exchange of ideas between
cultures, for they had seen enough to celebrate the ethnic
and religious diversity in their ranks. They taught each other
their trades and languages. They discarded their former
patriotisms. They were born again with new identities. Each
year they voted for who among them would lead. In every
land they traversed they respected the inhabitants. They
stole solely from the hostile. In that epoch where ignorance
loomed, they sought only treasure that would enhance
knowledge and preserve histories threatened with extinction.

Mojgan's story of Ali Baba, Kinbote said, proves the original to be less apocryphal than incomplete. There was no
"thief leader"; instead, they voted for their overall "Asim"
(عاسم), or protector, as well as the council of seven "Aqils"
(عاقل), or wise men. The treasures in the cave did include
precious metals and stones, but the majority consisted of
illuminated books, scrolls, maps, and musical and scientific
instruments. The cave itself was secured not by a magic
portal, but by a complicated system of pulleys requiring
the timing of two men working its central mechanism on
cue. The order of the Asim—commonly related as "open
sesame!"—was actually "iftah ya simsim!", with the latter
word's Semitic roots referring to the sesame seed but also to
modern Hebrew's "sisma" (שומשום), which means password.

Most importantly, the manuscript, Kinbote said, reveals the original story's "pattern of exaggeration . . . particularly that the Asim would, or could, condemn two of his men to death for unsuccessfully locating the thieving woodcutter Ali Baba's home." We need look no further, Kinbote continued, than the "unrealistic" story from Morgiana, the slave girl of Ali Baba's brother Cassim: She claimed she killed single-handedly thirty-seven thieves by pouring boiling oil upon them as they hid in adjacent crockery jars; it is incredible not one of the victims was alerted by the screams of the others.

Kinbote admitted his findings are not to be taken as strictly historical, highlighting that the number forty in this story may possess metaphorical and intertextual importance. Kinbote cited the forty days of rain preceding the Great Flood, the forty Moses spent on the mountain, the forty years the Israelites wandered the desert, Christ's forty nights fasting in the wilderness, or the forty days He was seen on earth following His crucifixion. So, too, Kinbote said, does the council of seven Aqils resonate with pilgrims' seven circumambulations of the Ka'ba in Mecca, the seventh heaven that Mohammed visited, the seven stones hurled at devil statues during the Hajj, the seven happy wives who bless a Pakistani marriage by touching the bride's dress, and, as evidenced within the *Nights* themselves, the seven voyages of Sinbad the Sailor.

Crawford informs this reporter that Kinbote said that Mojgan of Esfahan's story appears incomplete, and does not discuss each of the Forty in equal detail. In fact, Kinbote added, Mojgan cautions against both a yearning for precision and blind faith, reminding that what is told will never be more than a fraction of the truth, and that told fraction will ever be distorted by time, distance, and the human tendency to wish to hear what we wish to hear.

Mojgan continues the familiar story beyond what we all know. The night is quiet without a moon, and music and laughter tumble like an unravelling ball of string from where Ali Baba's guests dine. Among them is the Asim, disguised as a wealthy oil merchant. In the shadows of the courtyard hang the thirty-nine oil jars, their sides clicking and clinking as the camels and horses to which they're attached shove and spit for space at the trough. When the conniving slave girl Morgiana pours boiling oil into the first jar, the man inside looses an unforgettable scream. Out pop the other thirty-eight, wide eyed, from the jars in which they hide. Dogs bark. Alarm bells clang, smashing the silence into smithereens of ringing shouts and swords unsheathing. The footfalls of the guards thud on the ramparts. Certain of capture, the Badr hesitate, then speed, as sudden as second thoughts, into the forbidding safety of the desert. The poor Asim attempts to follow suit but is held at cutlass-point by Ali Baba himself.

Before you take your leave of my hospitality, Ali Baba declares, pray tell us who you are, and where you are going in such haste. The Asim replies: I am one who bears neither the obstinacy of nobility nor the promiscuity of opportunism, who wants neither to serve nor to lead, who believes justice is equal parts revenge and sympathy, who desires neither the weight of riches nor the liberty of poverty. For these reasons, I was chosen, unanimously, by my compatriots to be their leader, though only the great and good Allah himself can choose our fate for us. I am a simple Mandaean fletcher, from where the Tigris and Euphrates are at their farthest in their embrace, an expert at the hejazi bow, and a perpetual student of the movements of the stars. I am one of a company of forty noble commoners. Some of us are good, some are less so. Some have stories that do not bear repeating, while others' insist upon the telling. Of them all I will speak to you now.

My favoured are five orphan brothers from Samarkand, the eldest possessing the strength of three men, the second bearing a voice like the sun, the third an expert in speaking to animals, the fourth an endearing fool, and the fifth their young sister disguised as an insouciant boy, whose enduring masquerade brings a smile to our faces on a daily basis. There are three Mongol royal guards who were tasked by their master to escort Friar John of Pian de Carpine home, to Rome, to deliver to Pope Innocent IV this message: Come, great pope, and pay homage to the great Guyuk Khan. Alas, the pope's anger was coursed to these escorts of his emissary, and they fled as oarsmen on a Venetian galley that was later shipwrecked off the Cyrenaican coast. The eldest of our brotherhood is Simeon, an unpleasant man from Jerusalem who bears the wisdom of centuries heavily, waiting to glimpse the messiah and finally receive the solace of death.

The Forty

The youngest of our group is Anta'aneed, who knows not that he is a ghost, who has celebrated seven birthdays in my presence since he was slain at the age of five when his village in Balochistan was plundered. I met him myself in that land of orange orchards, as I travelled with my weapons less for valour than for money. Soon after, I helped defend Chittorgarh against the armies of the lecherous Sultan Alauddin Khilji, who had fallen in love with Queen Rani Padmini, whose beauty he'd been allowed to view only as a reflection in a mirror. I remember that siege, that hopeless night, that great immolation of the women who preferred death by their own hands to dishonour by another's; you could read by the light of their flames. With their women dead, the men of the fort had nothing to live for. Dressed in their saffron robes, they streamed out to face the outnumbering enemy, and I would have been slain with them had I not been injured and captured. I escaped my execution only because I acquired in their prison a Djellaba of Shadows, a splendid garment that does not render you so much invisible but as dark as the night. I won it in a game of knucklebones, from a lunatic Amazigh thief whose scent was so foul invisibility was insufficient. And so I found myself in a foreign land, shoeless, penniless, and countless cubits from home.

And now here I am before you. I have faced life, and turned my back on death, heard the songs of the heavens and seen the ends of the earth. But before you hasten to make my rescue futile, and quickly put me to the sword, as I know you will, I ask you, in the name of Allah—who is wise and merciful!—to see the story to the end of its telling. For I will share a secret history—of who dreamed our company of forty into being, and why.

The guests crowd around. Ali Baba nods. And the Asim continues his tale.

REBECCA WAIT

Wilderness

And sometimes it's not easy, because people come to you – 'I was unfaithful to my husband' or 'I lied to my friend' – and you have no idea what to tell them. You can't be on top of things all the time. Sometimes you just want to say, 'Well, what do you want me to do about it?' But you don't turn people away. I've known that from the start. However long it's been since your last meal, or your last proper rest, you're always available for them. It can be tough. But that's part of the deal.

What it's best to do when you're close to burned out is to offer vague reassurance – 'We might make the wrong choices, but it's never too late to turn things around' – whilst gently encouraging them to do the right thing. You don't need to go into specifics. Go on your way and be good in future. That kind of thing. But tread carefully. People don't like to be told what to do. That's something I learnt early on. If you make them feel like they've made the decision on their own – and you've just provided the impetus, or whatever – then they'll choose the good every time, and afterwards be pretty much ready to follow you to the ends of the earth.

Something else I've learnt. People love to do the right thing. Be as cynical as you like, most of them are decent at heart. I don't care what anybody else says. All people really want is to be shown how to be good, and to believe they're capable of goodness. I believe they are – I really do. That's why they keep coming to me. No one *aims* to be selfish. No one plans to be mean-spirited or unkind. Life can twist you about. But I won't be convinced anyone's lost. Stop for a moment, I tell them. Take a rest. I have a message for you.

My friends worry that I'm taking too much on, and they try to get me to slow down. But I think they understand really. You have a duty. When you're responsible for so many, you can't get caught napping, particularly with him prowling around. I was warned about him in the beginning: Sleep with one eye open. You can rest afterwards.

So I make myself keep going, because I know why I'm here. You can get through anything if you have a purpose.

It's been getting harder recently, though. Recently hasn't been so good. He's been around more and more and I feel it's beginning to get out of hand. It was simple at the start – I could shake him off or outsmart him with my hands tied behind my back. It was so easy it almost felt like a game. But it's been going on a while now, and it starts to wear you down. It would wear anyone down. And when it's late at night and you're exhausted it gets more and more difficult to ignore that sly voice, that wheedling persuasive voice telling you you're not up to it, you can't do it – that there's been some kind of mistake. Or sometimes it's that you can do it, but the truth is it won't make any difference. Not in the end. I've been knocking around for a long time, he says. Trust me.

All that negative energy – of course it gets to you. And when he's been on you pretty much non-stop for forty days and forty nights it gets kind of hard to tune him out. Pretty difficult to keep perspective like they say and weigh up all the good against the bad to save yourself from drowning. Forty days and forty nights of *you're nothing, you're nobody.* It's too much for anyone to take. And he wants you to eat, but even though you're starving you have to resist. So you tell him you can deal with the hunger. And he wants you to jump and let the angels break your fall. And you refuse, you tell him you will never test your Father, you will never jump – but the truth is, you won't do it because at this point you're not even sure about the angels. Whose side are they on?

The weight of the world is a lot for one person to carry. It's heavy, you know? It's really heavy.

And you find it's four a.m. and you have to get up in two hours, and you haven't slept again, haven't even been to bed. You're sitting alone and he's gone for a while but it doesn't seem to help. Then she's standing in the doorway, just standing there looking at you and saying 'Darling?' over and over, and you don't know what to tell her because you knew from the start how this ends

    'Darling?'

    and your Father's providing no help

    'Darling?'

KEVIN WILSON

What We Have Made: Celebrating the Fifth Birthday of Our Fortieth Child

Perhaps we hoped we would finally get it perfect with the fortieth child, but it's more likely that, by that point, we no longer worried about the logic of bringing baby after baby into the world. It went beyond biological imperative. We made children. We made forty children. We love each one and we pray that they love us in return.

The cake for the fortieth child is the size of a compact car. The five candles are so tiny that they look like pushpins placed on a map to signify places that we will never visit. How strange, we realize time and time again, that none of the forty children, save the twins and triplets, share the same birthday. Life has become a never-ending celebration of birth, a constant reminder that the things that we made keep going, will live long after we are gone. We made an army and they protect us from harm.

The *how* of making these children is not as interesting as you'd think. Twenty-five percent of the time, we were shocked to discover the fact that another child had taken up residence in our womb, having no memory of the actual conception. The *why* of making these children is a perfectly reasonable question, but, forty children later, we can't satisfactorily answer it. The only answer we can offer is simply another question. If you loved something with all of your heart, and it was possible for you, with very little help, to make more of these things, why wouldn't you keep doing it?

It is difficult to remember all of their names. Even if we simply assigned them their own number in the order of their birth, we're not sure that we could keep it straight. The difference between your seventeenth and eighteenth child is so negligible that one must allow for gaps in memory. To save us the embarrassment, we call all of them *Baby*. They call us Mom and Dad; it's easy for them to remember us. We call them Baby and they smile with the satisfaction of being named.

The first child was the hardest, all the pros and cons of bringing something into this world. We were in our early twenties and we feared that we would prove unsuitable as parents. We worried that we would ruin the child with our failings, no doubt given to us by our own parents. What finally compelled us, thank god, was the belief that this world, a meaningless vessel for our brief lives, was made important by our very existence. We made more of ourselves in order to justify the fact that we had no business being here, and, in the process, we earned the right to be alive. The decision finally made, the baby came easy and with such gratifying heft that it was less than a year before we were weighed down by the second.

It is impossible to keep track of them all, some of them already grown and with children of their own. We receive postcards from them and it takes full minutes before we can call forth the image of their specific face. But, once it comes to us, the flood of that single child washes over us, and we are ecstatic to know that, though they are spreading out across the world, the lines that connect us to them are elastic enough to never separate. They tell us, in these tiny scraps of paper, that they are having a wonderful time, and we know that, sooner rather than later, they will return to us and we will be made whole again.

For the fortieth child, everything is a hand-me-down. Every single wrapped present on the table today is simply a gift that the other children once cherished, their fingerprints burned into the object. It is the same, we guess, for the thirty-ninth child and the thirty-eighth child and every child except for the first. If they begrudge this fact, they do not reveal it to us. When the fortieth child unwraps one of these presents and places his hands upon it, it will be as if he is holding hands with every one of his brothers and sisters.

Not one of our children is deceased. We are lucky in this respect. We hope, now that we are in our seventies, that we might pass out of this world before any of them leave us. It is natural, to outlive your children, but when you make forty of them, you lose any right to what is normal for others. Some nights, we dream of our funeral, both of us dead at the exact same moment, the children processing in front of our caskets in a train so long that it seems that we will never be interred.

It is close enough to the fourth of July that the children are allowed the treat of sparklers. The youngest come to us with the unlit sticks, waiting for our lighters to sizzle the sparklers into existence. They run around the park, waving the hissing light in wide circles. There are so many children holding these sparklers that the park begins to look like a war zone, heavy with smoke that obscures their laughing, howling forms. From time to time, one of the children runs to us for more sparklers, for a kiss, for encouragement. We give them everything we have and they run away from us, fire in their hands.

People wonder about the expense of forty children. We have lived a life of bulk, of heavily doctored clothing, of homemade distractions. People pity our lack of funds, the fact that we never have the money to spend on ourselves, as if these children, these little creatures, have not been the greatest luxury we could ever have afforded. They want to know about the minutiae of our daily lives: transportation, food, baths. They want to know how we live a life that resembles anything close to normalcy, and we want to shake these people so violently that their teeth rattle. We want to turn them toward our forty children, each one beautiful and smiling and perfect, and we want to say, "Do you understand the magic of these children? Do you see that all of them are worth any amount of inconvenience and worry? How can you not wish for a life surrounded by people who think you created the world in which they live?"

It is not a blissful existence all of the time. Changing diapers for seven children at a time, all on a different schedule, never sleeping, eating only whatever they decide to forego . . . it becomes exhausting. For a while, we doubted the logic of our children, or perhaps we doubted our ability to care for them. And then, suddenly, around the tenth of eleventh child, we allowed our grip on the world to relax slightly. We allowed feral tendencies into our routine. Clothing became optional. Bathing became optional. They needed only to be able to read, speak, and stay alive. If they sometimes bit each other or us, if they sometimes pissed into our open mouths while we slept, if they sometimes stole candy from stores and extracted loose teeth along with the sticky caramel, we learned to accept it. We learned, actually, to love it. We became wild and the world became understandable to us. We became stronger than anything that might ruin us. We allowed trace amounts of disease into our bodies and were unaffected by it. The children that followed, they were ripples in a body of water that had no bottom to it.

The children fill their paper plates with an ocean of boiled shrimp. They tear apart the thin shells, the tiny legs, and they place the meat into their mouths and chew with great enthusiasm. They bite into the soggy ears of corn and feel the kernels give themselves over to the children's hunger.

They spear potatoes with their plastic forks and burn their tongues on the trapped heat. They hold links of sausage in their fists like sticks of dynamite. With forty children, every meal is a feast, the sound of chewing and digestion like a thousand crickets and frogs, a symphony that, to our ears, sounds exactly like we have composed it.

We did not stop at forty children. We have no need for round numbers, for symmetry. We simply stopped conceiving. It was a strange sensation, to be absent of expectation. The only thing inside of us was our own soul, and we worried that we were being punished for our excess. And, then, without the constant expansion of pregnancy, of a new child replacing the one that has suddenly grown, we experienced the miracle of observation, of noticing the children we already had as their hair grew and changed color, as their bodies accommodated their desire to mature, as they gained speech and motor skills and as they, despite all of this, never failed to fold into our arms and accept our embrace. If no child follows the fortieth, we are accepting of this future. Even God eventually rested.

Now, the other thirty-nine children surround the fortieth and they sing, in perfect harmony, "Happy Birthday." We watch our children as their voices escape from inside of them, a beautiful song that we have heard so many times that it sounds as natural as the wind. We hold each other, a few steps away from all of these children that are ours, are forever ours. They sing and sing, the fortieth child giggling and excited, waiting for the moment that the song ends and the world will resume spinning. In this moment, we know that we have made something perfect. We are two that made forty. We are the world that made, because of the depth of our love, forty unified worlds. Just as the song ends, the fortieth child sucks in a deep breath, all of the air in the universe, and he blows out the candles so forcefully that it seems like a magic trick. The children, our children, cheer, and then they push forward, closing ranks around the cake, and we watch them tear into the cake as if they could never be sated. We watch them move and shout and laugh and we want to put our arms around them and tell them that we loved each one from the moment they were born, from the moment we ever thought a life like this was possible. We wait for a few seconds and then we run to them and disappear inside of the shape they have made for us.

SIMON WINDER

The Picador 'Spinner'

I was raised in the tough Kent–Sussex border town of Tun-bridge Wells, a place fuelled by antiques thefts and with a political extremism all its own. In the 1970s it just clung to its old reputation as a last resting place for retired Imperial civil servants and soldiers, with the occasional man in a three-piece suit and deep-red skin trundling up and down the brick-pavement hills to the Hole-in-the-Wall pub or Binn's Tearooms. Knick-knack shops there today still keep that memory, full of brass plates, fire-tong sets, kukris and sandalwood gods shovelled out of the houses of the deceased by unentertained descendants. The elephant-foot umbrella stands and peacock fans have at last rotted away, but the imperishable brassware will probably still be viewed as a nadir of taste many centuries from now, quite possibly in the same shop.

In this strange place I had my life's entire course set by

walking one day, aged fifteen, into a very small bookshop and asking for a holiday job. The owner decided on a whim to say yes and I stayed there, working whenever I was around, until I was well into university. The shop was really alarmingly small, and felt crowded if (not a frequent event) there were more than about seven customers. It had two floor areas, joined by a narrow space filled with a cash desk. Every wall and every conceivable surface was crowded with books. A cast-iron circular staircase led to a dank basement where spare stock, a wrapping and boxing table, a spider-filled toilet and some spectacular ordering mistakes were located. Of course, most bookshop stock can be returned, but some smaller publishers still did firm-sale deals and a whole wall was devoted to unsold hardbacks of the great French historian Emmanuel Le Roy Ladurie's *Carnival in Romans*, his woefully unsuccessful follow-up to the salaciously marketed and involving *Montaillou*. This was a brutal reminder of how in southeast England there is a clear this-far-no-further on engaging with meticulous reconstructions of life in the Languedoc of yesteryear, an invaluable insight in my later life as a publisher.

The owner was a heroic figure, as I only now fully realize. A very refined, thoughtful, quite shy man who loved good writing and was realizing an ideal by having his own bookshop, he would only stock books he personally liked. So there were excellent sections on literary biography, cooking, gardens, plenty of classics and clever contemporary fiction. This was a fair identikit for a particular Tunbridge Wells consumer so the shop thrived in a modest way. There was another assistant, Eve, who was in fact a proper bookseller, in that she was always stock-checking, sending out parcels, replenishing the paper bags and so on, while I fulfilled the traditional assistant role of chatting to the owner, reading and sharing the responsibility with him of laughing at some of the deeply odd customers. Eve knew a great deal about esoterica and lovingly tended a section devoted to the rigours of Gurdjieff, Krishnamurti and Ouspensky. These were a surprising success – at least surprising to me in my total scornful ignorance. An important block of customers were indeed the sort of people who had had funny experiences as young men in Himalayan hill-stations or in the Malay jungle and who now managed to be both deeply dyed-in-the-wool while also keeping up a lively interest in mandalas, mystic flames or the Land Beyond – an important strand to the British Empire which remains under-examined. The elderly 'Glubb Pasha' would come in occasionally, camel-soldier extraordinary and a former commander of the Arab Legion, but now chiefly fascinated – if I remember correctly – by St Augustine's *City of God*.

Sometimes I think the whole place was a mirage – events and customers seem so implausible, the values so remote. Being a shop, we were painfully vulnerable to any passing figures just walking through the door: maniacs, drunks, the very lonely, petty thieves, fantasists – the reliable core of any decent independent bookstore. There was a very strange old lady, a child of Bloomsbury, who would come in looking for anything on Virginia Woolf and her friends. We had the horrible experience of selling her a volume of Woolf's letters in which we knew (because we had looked to see) there was a typically vicious joke about this lady's freakish appearance as a child.

We had quite an elaborate list of authors the owner just would not stock – James Hadley Chase, I remember, Barbara Cartland, almost anything derivative of television – and he had a slightly unfortunate way of conveying in his tone of voice what a social and intellectual failure the enquirer had to be to want such a thing. This gave a perhaps needless centrifugal force to our customer base, throwing off people left and right who never dared to return, but could be seen walking past, glaring in resentfully. I cannot have helped, with what I can be pretty sure must have been a pompous, cakey manner, shuddering and going an odd colour if anyone said the words 'Len Deighton'. On a rainy day in January my daily pay came quite close to the actual takings, but I would have spent the day chatting with the owner about some novel and generally used my money to buy a copy, so it was a bit more efficient than it appears.

At irregular, widely spaced intervals the large, dark antiques shop opposite us, which was generally closed, would magically light up. The owner, a compact and equable Armenian, would arrive with a client, reach a deal to sell him some Tang dynasty jade horse, and then turn out the light, lock up and disappear again for a few more weeks. Whenever this would happen we would studiously not notice, each presumably making some fervid private calculation as to how many years of our own turnover had just been conjured up with a handshake. This was a valuable lesson in understanding the futility of books as a business.

I don't think I was bored in that shop even for a second – I would create elaborate ziggurats of books in the window, carefully choosing the titles with my own taste at the time the only market research. So if I was reading a lot of works of coded gayness the windows would fill up with Ronald Firbank, Denton Welch, Baron Corvo, Jocelyn Brooke; if I was going through a phase of loving the idea of Virago (then in its pomp) it would be all Christina Stead, Dorothy Richardson, Storm Jameson. It is unclear how many customers these displays angled in (they probably created a force-field of distaste), but I liked to think I could dress a nice window.

Many hours were spent talking to reps and it was probably this almost as much as the shop itself that made me think I should become a publisher. I was hypnotized by the way the rep could unveil a season's worth of his new books, playing up strengths, masking weaknesses, carefully deriding celebrity tat he knew we would never take anyway, while cornering us into ordering a reckless pile of some theatrical memoir.

I just missed the hyena-pack frenzy of *The Country Diary of an Edwardian Lady*, a book which had in 1977 sold simply astronomical quantities, filled with nicely observed watercolours of nosegays and robin red-breasts and which defined a sort of mad gentility for years to come, reflected in spin-off decorative napkins, coasters, toilet-brush covers and so on. But having missed the main event, I was in the perfect position to relish the after-shocks as rep after rep with a suitably faux-excited patter would flourish a special 'blad' announcing some further low-self-esteem *Country Diary* knock-off. By early 1979 there cannot have been an artist in the country not engaged in painting horse-chestnuts a-bursting from their shells or red squirrels at frolic, all flanked by hand-written notes of the changing seasons. We would come up with ever more elaborate jokes about the true identities of these painters, press-ganged by deranged publishers into faking a sudden interest in tomtits or the glories of the hollyhock: perhaps some massive, pornography-raddled lighthouse-keeper watercolourist, or a distinguished Academician fighting off nasty blackmail attempts, or Willem de Kooning. In any event, I learned early the joy of rep selling – when to elaborately 'shoot' a book you know the bookseller does not want anyway, when to evoke pity for the uselessness of your list and secure a 'mercy' sale for something, anything. I loved discount terms, sales points, jacket designs. I even loved the giant leather bag full of selling sheets, heavy samples, packets of Rolos, catalogues, little knowing that I would be staggering around with one myself only too soon, when my old, innocent derision of hopeless marketing material would seem a lifetime away.

The highlight of the year – and with a directness and excitement that now seems sadly remote – was the Booker Prize shortlist. I was there for the great Godzilla vs. The Smog

Monster battles between *Earthly Powers* and *Rites of Passage*, *Midnight's Children* and *The White Hotel*, *Schindler's Ark* and *An Ice-Cream War*. I read and loved Alice Thomas Ellis and Timothy Mo, we sold lashings of J. L. Carr's *A Month in the Country* and Molly Keane's *Good Behaviour*, wonderful novels that made our ever-narrowing customer-base purr with happiness. The arguments seemed endless about these books and the stakes oddly high. I can still remember every detail of their covers and could – if suitably hypnotized – probably come up with their ISBNs. I loved them as literature, but I also loved them as business.

And it is this – by a roundabout route – that brings me to Picador's fortieth birthday. We had very little room in the shop, but we did have a big plastic 'spinner', a stand shaped a bit like a rocket, that could be turned (although 'spun' would be an exaggeration), and was full of Picador books. This was for the tenth anniversary of Picador, which, as I was myself at that point only in my late teens, gave Picador for me a near-antiquarian patina of age and grandeur. It was crammed with the then gods of the Picador pantheon: Calvino, McEwan, Hoban, Musil – and was a bit of a disaster, as these were just the kind of writers who, by a variety of criteria, made the people of Tunbridge Wells bristle. As we had no computer system we used to work out how old a book was by looking at the paper along its top to see if it had changed to a sort of yellowy colour, but did not look so shabby that it could not be returned. Alas, I have a clear memory of Musil failing this test. I am not sure whose idea ordering the 'spinner' was (which quite rapidly jammed and spun no more – and became much loved in its futility from that time on). It may have been mine as I had a somewhat sick enthusiasm for publishing brands. I certainly remember that my devotion to Penguin Modern Classics at one point led me during a stock-check to order up the entire backlist, temporarily filling the shop with heaps of Sholokhov, Cendrars, Kubin and a gigantic invoice. The problem of paying this was rectified only by my then filling in a substantial returns request and getting these unsellable Masters back in their boxes and off to be pulped by a no doubt irritated Penguin.

This is hardly the most delicate context to raise this point, but we had kept a number of High Modernist Picador titles on the shelf before the magnificent 'spinner' arrived, as part of a long-running joke about books we were comically unlikely to sell. They sat there for years, the paper of their tops a sort of baked russet and no longer even faintly returnable. I particularly remember Gilbert Sorrentino's *Mulligan Stew*, Elias Canetti's *Auto-da-Fé*, John Cowper Powys' *A Brazen Head* and Guillermo Cabrera Infante's *Three Trapped Tigers* as being sources of almost infinite laughter, as they very slowly buckled, curled and convulsed on the shelf and then were given pride of place in the 'spinner'. This is all so shamefully ignorant I really should stop. *Three Trapped Tigers* particularly seemed so *exactly* what nobody in Tunbridge Wells would ever buy even by accident or a trick that it became, using the perverse standards of the shop, an object of affection and pride.

For some two years off and on I sat next to the 'spinner' and I came to love Calvino, pick up a guarded and partial interest in Canetti, be amazed by Tobias Wolff's first short-story collection and begin a perhaps abusive yet fun relationship with John Cowper Powys. I also had my mind and worldview gradually taken over by the great Russell Hoban, whose *Kleinzeit* I picked off the 'spinner' – perhaps at a point when it no longer spun, making the book nearest to my shoulder unvarying and insistent.

This was all very many years ago. I became a publisher (even, in a spirit of atonement, running Penguin Modern Classics) and an actual Picador author, but I am not sure I have ever felt closer to the heart of why books matter than when working in that shop.

NAOMI WOOD

Ghosts

Pia threw her jacket and bag onto the back seat. The car had a mushroomy smell, as if, unattended for the day, something might have started growing in the upholstery seams. It was this heat; so late in September. But Pia kept the windows up; it felt safer like that.

As she circled the car park, Pia caught the measured voice of the Radio 4 newsreader. 'Today, scientists across the world are facing a revolution in physics. Neutrinos – ghostly subatomic particles, which pass through our bodies all the time – have broken the universe's fundamental speed limit: the speed of light.' The story continued as she queued for the exit with all the other lecturers in their little cars. The newsreader kept on using the word *ghostly*, which Pia found odd, since it seemed to suggest a life, a death, and a botched resurrection – a metaphor she didn't think scientists would like. She wondered how many of these particles had ghosted through her this morning, as she had shovelled the coffee into the cafetière, broke the eggs into the warming pan, pegged the laundry to the clothesline. How quickly, she wondered, did they whizz through hair, scalp, cranial vault, brain tissue? And she wondered, too, if their course might be slowed by the cloudy melancholia that had descended on her today, on the morning of her fortieth birthday.

Free of the car-park, Pia executed her Fiat Punto through a cute right turn and headed towards Bethnal Green. She supposed that these subatomic bits would still be travelling through her, at guileless and impressive zoom through skin, membrane, and into the car's upholstery, even as she travelled at a speed which, she saw from the speedometer, was over the limit. Now she rolled down the window and a hot breeze streamed in. Autumn had gone backwards into summer, and the trees' rusted leaves once again cupped a whole heap of heat. It must be sending the animals nuts.

Perhaps she should call Daniel and ask him to delay their restaurant booking. But then she would have to stop the car to make the phone call, and irritation – that faint thrill of the world not behaving quite to her liking – was in her. Pia pressed the accelerator, moving the car along Mare Street, noticing the children's drawings overhanging the traffic lights. There were pictures of snails and tortoises, accompanied by exquisitely pathetic lettering, urging motorists to *SLO DOWN!* Pia grinned through their commandments, speeding up.

She was dying, really, to be at home; it had been a day that had felt longer than its eight hours. The melancholy that had met her this morning was no better for it being expected; all year she had been dreading the time when she would, irrevocably, turn forty. All year, in fact, she'd felt rather hollowed-out. Where did it come from? This feeling of constant fatigue? Pia felt sleep-deprived and yet she was sleeping more than ever. Perhaps she was depressed – as if what the neutrinos were travelling through was indeed a soggy toilet-roll of sad brain tissue. She could be depressed; Daniel had said she had a proclivity towards depression – which she always thought was a sweet way of expressing it, as if it were a penchant for chocolate, or ice-cream.

Pia was now doing forty in a thirty zone but she knew there were no cameras here. Expecting the traffic to be better, she took the earlier exit at Queensbridge rather than Kingsland Road; it wasn't. The feeling was a kind of bereavement, that was it: to be facing a time so loosened from any expectation of joy. Despite some of her bluer moods Pia had essentially been a person of optimism. Today, there was only a singular feeling that everything worth happening had already happened.

Some of the shops were still boarded up after the August riots: a pawn shop, a sportswear store, an off-licence. It hadn't just been kids this summer, it had been adults, too, playing at this childish game of consequence-less theft. What a strange year, this; adults regressing into childhood; autumn reverting to summer; neutrinos overtaking the speed of light, time going backwards; all this as Pia, at forty, raced toward her grave.

When she hit Dalston Junction she turned up the radio. The newsreader's accent was flat and colourless. '. . . Neutrinos travelling the seven hundred and thirty kilometre journey from the CERN Institute in France to the Gran Sasso Institute in Italy arrived sixty nanoseconds earlier than they would have if they had been travelling at light speed.' Pia slipped into the left lane, only to be frustrated by a large London bus that felt the need to take up two. 'If their findings are correct, it could render Einstein's theory null, and make, at least theoretically, time travel possible.'

Everything had reached a standstill. Pia's fingers drummed the wheel. She thought about bending time backwards, about slipping into her life-already-lived, watching as effect morphed into its cause. Sitting in gridlock, she travelled back over her fortieth birthday: how her car would re-spiral the car park's exit; how the candle flames on her birthday cake would illuminate at lunchtime; how the coffee would be drunk before she had made it; how she would eat the omelette before watching the albumen and yolk slide back into the unsplit shell; how the laundry would dampen rather than dry; how they would make love, this morning, her and Daniel Cord; make their twin journeys from being clothed to being naked, from orgasm to the first hints of arousal (which she had tried, at first – though she didn't know why – to push away); how, just before he began to touch her, for minutes, lone and awake, she would be looking at the bald white ceiling and marvelling at how deep her unhappiness went. *I am middle-aged,* she would think, as Daniel's snores combed the air, *and want not to be.* Then she would be knifed awake by the thought that had woken her: *Please, God! Let me have it all again!*

The traffic was clearing as Pia turned left and started to speed along Ball's Pond Road, escaping Dalston and entering the leafier groves of Canonbury. The scientist being interviewed had a gentle Swiss tilt to his flawless English. 'What we are proposing is that the neutrinos might have travelled through a fourth – thus far unobserved – dimension of space. Imagine,' Pia pulled up sharply against the suddenly still traffic, 'that this fourth dimension is flat, but quantum fluctuations have made it ripple, like the surface of the sea. Just as flying fish may take a shortcut against the current by skipping along the crests of the waves, this is what the neutrinos might be doing – freeing themselves of the dense matter below and flying quicker through another matter altogether: a fourth dimension.'

Pia thought the metaphor quite lovely: she imagined the neutrino flying with all the grace of the flying fish, breaking from the saltwater and soaring through the air, its silver-flecked tail flashing in the light, its white belly hitting the next wave with a slap. Enlivened by the metaphor, and flying into the slipstream of the bus lane, Pia went faster than she should, surfing the crests of each car, freed from the traffic to her side.

Without any warning a large truck, nose-heavy without

its container, suddenly pulled out directly in front of her. Pia slammed the brakes and swerved. Her head and body sprang forward from the seat, travelling hard through time and space though the car had, metres from when she had first applied the brakes, come to a stop. The seatbelt burned a line across her chest. And then, just as suddenly, the course was snapped into reverse: her neck whipped backward, and her body began to close the space behind it. Odd, to be thinking of all those thousands of neutrinos that had coursed through her now streaming back through her organs and bones.

Her head hit the back of the seat and, in time, she became still. Her eyes closed. The world went black and quiet. She let go. Giving in, she ghosted back through memory. She drank the coffee, ate the omelette, took down the laundry still damp. Her mind skipped backwards faster still, with all the flight of the flying fish: the births of her kids, her marriage to Daniel, getting her doctorate, falling in love for the first time at university. Now that her future was her past, she knew exactly what was to come, and the thrill of anticipation only made the feelings all the more exquisite. To wake up; to be in this stilled car; to be racing towards a restaurant dinner she had no mind to think about; in short, to be in time, meant facing a future Pia had no possession of. Or perhaps to wake up meant to find herself dead, her head bloodied on the steering-wheel, all time stopped. But then, like the flying fish wrenched out of water, she was pulled back down into the matter below.

*

There was a man outside her window. He was speaking. He peered in, looking afraid. Sound came back to the world. 'You OK?' She touched herself as if incapable of feeling things without the administration of her hands. Her hands, there they were; her stomach, her shoulders, her face. He said again, 'You OK?'

'I think I have whiplash.'

'You want to call someone? AA? Ambulance?'

'No.'

'Sure?'

'Yes. I'm not far from home. I'll be all right till then.' They politely squabbled about whether this was a good idea, then the man left and drove away. She took a deep breath and began again the drive home.

On her street the September leaves were golden, red, green. The sun caked them in light. Pia came to a stop outside their flat. She held her neck, massaging it; stepped out onto the warm tarmac. Keys and wallet and phone were gathered around the footwell, as if after a flood. Groaning, she bent down to gather them back into her bag. She stepped gingerly toward her house; conscious of herself.

The hall was cool, much cooler than the outside. 'Daniel?'

'Hi,' he said, his voice arcing from another room.

There was a card on the side. 'Happy 41st', it said. The card was from her mother.

'She'll be forgetting your name next,' said Daniel, behind her.

The hot band of the seatbelt had begun to fade. She wanted to tell him something, what was it that she wanted to tell him? Just that she wanted to go forward; that she could no more ghost through the time she had left than the time she had passed through. Something about the accident lent itself to privacy; she would not tell him. Instead she kissed him. Though it was autumn his mouth was warm with summer sun. Particles ghosted through these lips, both his and hers. Pia stayed there for longer than she had done this morning, before she had turned away from him, begun to dress, gone to make coffee, the omelette, hung the laundry on the line. 'You okay?' he asked, just as the driver had.

'Yes,' she said.

'Come on, then,' he said. 'Time waits for no man.'

She went upstairs to change.

GERARD WOODWARD

Mrs Box

It was my fortieth birthday, and I'd been given notice to quit by my landlady, Mrs Box. That's not her real name, I just call her that because she is very square, clumpy, and she likes to put things inside other things. I'd been a tenant of Mrs Box's for over three years (around forty months, actually), and had thought I might spend the rest of my life inside Mrs Box's box-like rooms. But then she said to me one day that she had to sell the house. She was very honest and straightforward about it. Like a box she can be open or closed, and this time she was open, and you could look inside her and see every-thing she was thinking and feeling. The feelings were very few, and the thoughts were square and clearly defined. She said she was being very generous with her terms, and had had a solicitor draw up a contract which gave me three months to find somewhere else to live. Three months, she said, was very generous. It is more usually six weeks. But in view of the fact I had been such a good tenant over the years, and had never been late with the rent, she was allowing me double the usual notice.

I had grown fond of my rooms. The house was a bit square and characterless, with its beige pebbledash and brown roof tiles, but it had an unusually large garden for a house of its type. Most other houses on the estate had tiny gardens, with hardly room to fit a sandpit or garden swing. But mine had a long lawn, a pond and two wild areas. The children loved it, when they lived there.

I felt rather upset about having to leave, and resentful that Mrs Box could just pick up my life, turn it upside down and shake it until I fell out. I heard a rumour that she wasn't planning to sell the house at all, and that instead she was going to convert it into five different flats. She could make more money that way. Instead of having one big box with a golden egg in it, she could have five small boxes, but each with the same-sized golden egg. It made good financial sense.

When I confronted Mrs Box with this information, she smiled in a rather pitying sort of way, and told me that really, her business affairs were no concern of mine.

'I hope you realize that these are difficult times,' she said, 'and that this isn't easy for any of us.'

I thought about that last statement, and decided that it wasn't true. It was very easy for Mrs Box, because her own life wasn't being turned upside down and shaken. And I thought nothing is difficult for her, because she doesn't do anything, apart from take money from me.

She was wearing one of her business outfits when she said this, a pink woollen jacket and a black skirt which, I couldn't help thinking, was far too short for a woman of her age, though the outfit did make her look younger. She could be mistaken for someone loveably bookish, at a glance, with her colourful gear and her heavy glasses, her blonde hair cut into a fashionable bob. She could have been a librarian at a library specializing in something arcane and bohemian. She could have been a poet's lover, a sculptor's muse. With her golden moustache she could have been – cigarillo between red lips – a hostess of a smoky seraglio. But no, she was a chartered accountant. I don't know how I knew that.

I once took in a dog. A little wire-haired yappy thing from a dogs' home. I knew it was against the rules but I thought that if he lived with me long enough before Mrs Box discovered him, he might seem so integral to the house her heart would melt along with mine. But Mrs Box is a stickler for rules. She put her foot down, and Trevor was sent back to the dogs' home. This isn't easy for any of us, is it, Mrs Box? No, not at all.

Shortly after the departure of Trevor, she gave me a gift. It arrived in a long, prettily wrapped box with a golden ribbon. Perhaps I've misjudged Mrs Box, I thought as I unwrapped it. She understood the pain I was feeling and had given me something to make me feel better. But her gift sent a chill through me. It was a Black and Decker hedge-trimmer.

Mrs Box had always worried about the hedge, thinking that if it was left untrimmed it would act as an invitation to burglars. Rather than pay someone to do it, she had asked me (always with that 'this is difficult for all of us' sincerity in her voice) if I wouldn't mind trimming it once in a while. But all I had in the shed was a pair of rusty shears. The hedge-trimmer gift was a jokey way for Mrs Box (who rarely displayed a sense of humour) to encourage me to trim the hedge, but she might as well have sent me a sword, or a machine gun. I was not prepared for the contained violence of the hedge-trimmer, and put it under the stairs, unused.

Three months. I didn't even bother looking for somewhere else to live. I had no money for a deposit and I had a bad credit history. I knew the only place I could find, at best, would be a damp bedsit in a crowded block somewhere. If I looked. I doubted I would even get my deposit back from Mrs Box. I've never had a deposit back from a landlord; they always find some reason or other. One held on to it because there was too much dust on top of the wardrobe. I didn't argue. I never argue. All I want is a quiet life.

I have tried, many times, to visualize an impossible thing – Mrs Box sitting down at her MFI workstation and writing a cheque for four hundred pounds, made payable to me. My deposit. But like I said, I can never picture it.

So with empty pockets I was getting ready to face the world. I had packed my life into boxes, all of them too small, but had nowhere to go. I was wondering if I could put

Mrs Box to the test and hold my ground, refuse to shift, nail myself in, do battle with the bailiffs and whoever else might descend, when a rather unexpected thing happened. I won forty million pounds on the lottery.

Forty million pounds. Forty million pounds. If I said it forty million times I would still be unable to believe it. But I won forty million pounds on a double rollover. My numbers were 40, 20, 10, 5, 8 and 4. As it was my fortieth birthday I decided to pick forty and all its factors. And it worked.

So my problems with accommodation were solved. I told no one about my win, and I chose the 'no publicity' option. I was given good accountants and tax advisers. I moved into a posh hotel while I looked for a house to buy. I put all my boxes into storage.

I didn't want to move far. In fact I could hardly bear to leave my town. There are some nice houses on the outskirts. I live in an ancient market town, and there are several old manor houses, Victorian super-villas, stately homes of the local gentry and the tycoons of days gone by. I bought one just beyond the trading estate, hidden behind a copse of trees and surrounded by pastures and paddocks. Nothing too ostentatious – five bedrooms, three reception rooms, a spacious hallway, so big I could have fitted the whole of Mrs Box's house into it. There was a stable wing that had already been converted into flats. There were garages that could take a whole fleet of limousines. And the grounds stretched all around the house for almost as far as I could see.

And all that came to less than half a million. I still had thirty nine and a half million left. I couldn't think what to do with it. All I knew was that buying my new house had given me a taste for buying houses.

Though I did buy a dog. Well, not exactly bought – like Trevor he came from the dogs' home and so cost nothing, but I gave the dogs' home a donation of fifty thousand pounds. The manager nearly wept when I gave her the cheque.

I employed a husband and wife as gardener and housekeeper, and let them live in one of the flats, at no charge. The housekeeper, Mrs Winn, did some cooking for me as well as keeping the house tidy.

Sometimes I took the dog for a walk into town, just to look at the shops and have something to do. It was odd, but I had lived in the town nearly all my life, and I didn't really know anyone. Old friends had moved on. My parents were both dead. I had no other family. My wife, of course, had moved away and taken the children with her. I hadn't told her about my money, not yet.

Otherwise I just had a few nodding acquaintances, people I sometimes met in the pub and would see in the town centre, pass the time of day with, mostly by talking about the dog, Charlie.

'Where are you living now?' they would say. 'I heard Mrs Box threw you out.'

'Yes. I found a little place behind the trading estate,' I

would reply. I'd still told no one about the win on the lottery, and was enjoying my anonymity, especially with the nodding acquaintances. They didn't know they were talking to a multi-millionaire, they just thought it was me, the same me I'd always been.

I knew where Mrs Box lived. She lived in one of the modern estates on the opposite side of town, in a very boxy house. Her road was called Cinnamon Drive, and there were about forty houses in it, mostly detached, with car ports at the front, a little patch of grass and shrubs to the side, and no separation between front garden and pavement. I liked to walk past her house and laugh quietly to myself at how small it was, compared to the house I lived in now. I encouraged Charlie to lift his leg on her lawn, but he usually couldn't be bothered. Not that it would have been very sufficient revenge if he had. I bore no animosity towards Mrs Box, though I couldn't help thinking about what would have happened to me if I hadn't won the lottery that day.

One day I noticed a For Sale sign in the front garden of the house next door to Mrs Box. When I enquired at the estate agent's office, I was surprised at how cheap it was. One hundred and forty thousand pounds. With all my millions I could buy that house and hardly notice a difference to my bank balance.

So I did.

The house was very similar to Mrs Box's. It had big windows, knock-through lounge, laurel bushes, a burglar alarm, hard standing for cars. I never saw inside it. I didn't want Mrs Box to know I'd bought the house next door to her, so I got my housekeeper Mrs Winn to do all the dealings on my behalf. And I thought about all the things I could do to Mrs Box, now that I had possession of the left-hand side of her life. I could move a difficult family in there, one that had been evicted from a rundown council estate for burning their neighbours' cars; I could turn it over to the council as a safe house for recently released paedophiles, or a probation hostel, the sort of place serial killers live after they've served a life sentence. I could have done many, many things like that, but in the end I did nothing. I paid Mr and Mrs Winn to go round there once a month and keep everything looking smart, inside and out. They were both sworn to secrecy, and told not to mention my name to Mrs Box should they ever meet her.

I decided to maintain the emptiness of the house for ever. She would have nobody for a neighbour on that side, and yet the house would be carefully maintained, the gardens mown, the hedges trimmed, the curtains washed at decent intervals, to make it seem no different from all the other well-kept houses in Cinnamon Drive.

My housekeeper said it was surprising how dirty a house could get even with no one living in it. Where does the dirt come from, she wondered. I wondered as well, but I couldn't think of an answer.

That might have been the end of it, had not another house in Cinnamon Drive come up for sale a few weeks later. So I bought that one as well. I still had my thirty nine million pounds. And I did the same thing – maintained it as an empty house, keeping it clean and spruce, but allowed no one to live there. And then quite a few more came on the market all at once, like they do sometimes in those sorts of roads. A little vending mania seems to take hold among the neighbours, they fall under the spell of some sort of property god and feel they must become buyers and sellers. While there's still time.

I bought the lot. Over a period of two years I bought nine houses in Cinnamon Drive, and left all of them empty. The street was slowly depopulating. I had some fun employing people to give the appearance of habitation. I paid someone to go, once a week, at odd times, to one of the houses, looking as though he'd just come back from a business trip. He just had to stay there overnight, and leave the next day. I paid one lady to turn up at one of the houses with a boot full of shopping, again once a week, roughly, to give the appearance the house was inhabited by a regular person.

Mrs Box would see these signs of suburban life carrying on as normal, and need never suspect that anything untoward was happening.

The following year the house on the other side of Mrs Box came up for sale. I bought it. Now I possessed both sides of Mrs Box's life. Left and right. She had no neighbours, just empty houses either side. Over the following three years I bought every house that came up for sale in Cinnamon

Drive. I owned more than half the street. And I continued to keep them empty, though maintained to look occupied. I continued to employ my retinue of mock-neighbours to come and go. I paid someone to wash a car here, to a mow a lawn there. I even got a little family with young children to pop in and out of one of the houses in Cinnamon Drive, at irregular intervals. On the remaining houses I am beginning to put a little pressure. I have sent leaflets round promising the best prices should the owners be thinking of selling.

This is what I imagine happening – over however many years it might take, I will buy every house in Cinnamon Drive, and leave it empty, though I will provide the necessary actors to give the impression that it is lived in. Eventually, Mrs Box will be the only resident. She will live completely alone. And if there is time I will buy the houses in the neighbouring streets as well. If I managed my money carefully I could buy all the houses on the estate. And all the while the estate will seem crowded and buzzing. I will put lights on with timers in all the houses, have the sounds of television and music blaring. The occasional group of children playing in a front garden. Then, when the time is right, and when Mrs Box is rather old, I will end the pretence. No more actors, or lights on time switches. The whole estate will fall into silence, and Mrs Box will find herself walking down a dead street with no lights in any of the houses. She will find herself miserably and terrifyingly alone. If I had the money I would buy the whole town and leave her its only inhabitant.

Mrs Box

O Mrs Box, Mrs Box, going from house to house in her dressing gown, her fashionable bob ruffled and askew, wondering where everyone has gone, wondering if the whole world has died, wondering if she'd slept for a thousand years – what pretty madness is this, a whole town, an ancient market town, reduced to nothing but a forest of empty boxes, empty, rattling, echoey boxes. The thought fills me with a shameful warmth. Mrs Box the only living soul, apart from me.

She knocks on every door she can find. There is no one in. The schools and shops are empty, because I have bought the whole town. Then, tears falling from her wobbly eyes, she wanders through the deserted trading estate and out the other side, and finds my house, behind the copse of trees, at the end of its long drive. She walks between the startling and brilliant lawns, aware that these are no longer guarantees of occupancy. It might be like all the other empty houses behind their perfect lawns. But she knocks anyway.

And I let her in. We have a good old talk.

THE CONTRIBUTORS

Megan Abbott is the award-winning author of the novels *Die a Little*, *The Song Is You*, *Queenpin* (which won the 2006 Mystery Writers of America Edgar Allan Poe Award), *Bury Me Deep* (nominated for the 2010 Edgar Award and the *Los Angeles Times* Book Prize), and *The End of Everything*. Her most recent novel is *Dare Me*. She also writes short stories and non-fiction, and is the editor of the Edgar-nominated *A Hell of a Woman: An Anthology of Female Noir*, featuring original tales by twenty-five mystery and crime authors.

Shalom Auslander was raised in Monsey, New York. Nominated for the Koret Award for writers under thirty-five, he has published articles in *Esquire*, the *New York Times Magazine*, *Tablet*, and the *New Yorker*, and has had stories aired on NPR's *This American Life*. He is the author of the short-story collection *Beware of God*, the memoir *Foreskin's Lament*, and the novel *Hope: A Tragedy*, all published by Picador. He lives in New York.

John Banville was born in Wexford, Ireland, in 1945. He is the author of fifteen novels published by Picador including *The Sea*, which won the 2005 Man Booker Prize. He was recently awarded the Franz Kafka Prize. He lives in Dublin.

The Contributors

A Chicago native, **Dave Boling** has been a journalist in the Pacific Northwest since 1980. Prior to that, he worked as a logger, iron-worker, boat-builder, bartender, bouncer, short-order cook, painter, and college football coach. He is the author of the bestselling novel *Guernica*, published by Picador. He lives on the Olympic Peninsula in Washington state.

Robin Black's debut collection, *If I Loved You, I Would Tell You This*, published by Picador, was shortlisted for the 2010 Frank O'Connor International Story Award. She lives in Philadelphia and is in the process of completing a novel.

John Butler has written and directed award-winning shorts for the Irish Film Board and directed and co-wrote the 6-part TV sketch show *Your Bad Self*. He is an occasional columnist and interviewer for the *Irish Times* and his writing has appeared in the *Dublin Review*, the *San Francisco Chronicle* and on NPR. John is the author of *The Tenderloin*, published by Picador, and lives in London.

Sarah Butler is in her early thirties and lives in Manchester. She runs a consultancy which develops literature and arts projects that explore and question our relationship to place. She has been writer in residence on the Central Line, the Greenwich Peninsula, and at Great Ormond Street Hospital, and has taught creative writing for the British Council in Kuala Lumpur. *Ten Things I've Learnt About Love*, her first novel, will be published in twelve languages around the world, and in the UK by Picador.

The Contributors

Emma Chapman was born in 1985 and grew up in Manchester. She studied English Literature at Edinburgh University, followed by a Masters in Creative Writing at Royal Holloway, University of London. After university, she travelled in Scandinavia, and she currently lives in Perth, Western Australia. Her first novel, *How To Be a Good Wife*, will be published by Picador in 2013.

Kate Clanchy was born and grew up in Scotland but now lives in England. She is a popular poet: her collections *Slattern*, *Samarkand*, and *Newborn* have brought her many literary awards and an unusually wide audience. She is also the editor of *The Picador Book of Birth Poems*. She has also written extensively for Radio 4, and reviews and writes comment for the *Guardian*.

Howard Cunnell has a Ph.D. from the University of London, and was previously a Leverhulme Fellow at the University of Sussex. He is the editor of Jack Kerouac's *On the Road: The Original Scroll*, which the *New York Times* described as 'the living version for our time', and the author of a novel, *The Sea on Fire*, published by Picador. A former professional scuba-diving instructor, he lives in London with his wife and children.

Edward Docx was born in 1972 and lives in London. He is the author of *The Calligrapher*, which was highly acclaimed and widely translated, and two novels published by Picador, *Self Help*, long-listed for the 2007 Man Booker Prize, and most recently *The Devil's Garden*.

The Contributors

Will Eaves was born in Bath in 1967. He is the author of three novels published by Picador, *The Oversight* (2001), *Nothing To Be Afraid Of* (2005), and *This is Paradise* (2012), and a collection of poems, *Sound Houses* (2011). For many years he was the arts editor of the *Times Literary Supplement*. He now teaches at the University of Warwick.

Max Egremont was born in 1948 and studied Modern History at Oxford University. As well as four novels, he is the author of *The Cousins* and *Balfour: A Life of Arthur James Balfour*. His acclaimed biography of Siegfried Sassoon was published by Picador in 2005 and his most recent work is *Forgotten Land: Journeys Among the Ghosts of East Prussia*, also published by Picador.

A former bookseller and editor, **Stuart Evers** is the acclaimed author of the collection *Ten Stories About Smoking*, which won the 2011 London Book Award, and the novel *If This Is Home*, both published by Picador. He lives in London.

Ellen Feldman, a 2009 Guggenheim Fellow, is the author of *The Boy Who Loved Anne Frank*, *Scottsboro*, which was shortlisted for the Orange Prize for Fiction, and *Next To Love*, all published by Picador. She lives in New York City with her husband.

Suzette Field was born in 1978 in Los Angeles. One of her earliest memories is sitting on Michael Jackson's lap in his studio while he was recording *Thriller*. In 1996 she moved to London where she ran a cinema in a converted warehouse. Since 2000 she has organized parties under the auspices of The Modern Times Club and latterly The Last Tuesday Society. The Society's legendary séances, crying parties and masked balls now regularly attract 3,000 revellers. Suzette also has a curios shop, gallery, and museum in Hackney. Picador are publishing her guide to literature's best parties, *A Curious Invitation*, to coincide with our fortieth birthday. She lives in Muswell Hill, North London, and has two children.

Annie Freud grew up in London and graduated in English and European Literature at the University of Warwick. She is the author of the poetry collections *The Mirabelles* and *The Best Man That Ever Was*, both published by Picador. She has one daughter, May.

Richard House is a lecturer in the Department of English at the University of Birmingham. He is the author of the forthcoming quartet of novels, 'The Kills', to be published by Picador in 2013.

Jackie Kay was born in Edinburgh in 1961 and grew up in Glasgow. She has written all her life. Several of her adult poetry collections have won or been shortlisted for awards across the board. Her first novel for children, *Strawgirl*, a lyrical slice of magical realism, was a huge critical success. Picador publish her first novel, *Trumpet*, which won the Author's Club First Novel

The Contributors

Award and the *Guardian* Fiction Prize, her memoir, *Red Dust Road*, her short-story collections *Why Don't You Stop Talking* and *Wish I Was Here*, her poetry collection *Fiere*, and her most recent work, the short-story collection *Reality, Reality*. Jackie lives in Manchester with her son.

Ian Kelly has written prize-winning biographies of Casanova, Beau Brummell, and Antonin Carême. He combines this with acting, from the art-historian in Lee Hall's *The Pitman Painters* to Hermione's father in the final instalments of the Harry Potter films. His new biography, *Mr Foote's Other Leg: Comedy, tragedy and murder in Georgian London*, is also published by Picador.

Gavin Knight has written for the *Guardian*, *Newsweek*, *Esquire*, *The Times*, *Prospect* and many other publications. His first book, published by Picador, is *Hood Rat*, an investigation of Britain's hidden underclass in London, Manchester, and Glasgow.

Belinda McKeon, an award-winning playwright, was born in Ireland in 1979. She studied literature at Trinity College, Dublin, and is a contributor to the *Irish Times*. McKeon has an MFA from Columbia University and lives in Brooklyn with her husband. Her first novel, *Solace*, published by Picador, was the Bord Gáis Energy Irish Book of the Year 2011.

Charlotte Mendelson was born in 1972 and grew up in Oxford. Picador publish her three novels. Her first, *Love in*

Idleness, was shortlisted for the Orange Prize. Her second, *Daughters of Jerusalem*, won the Somerset Maugham Award and the John Llewellyn Rhys Prize, and she was shortlisted for the *Sunday Times* Young Writer of the Year Award. Her third, *When We Were Bad*, was shortlisted for the Orange Broadband Prize for Fiction 2008. Charlotte lives in London with her family.

Stuart Nadler is a graduate of the Iowa Writers' Workshop, where he was awarded a Truman Capote Fellowship and a Teaching-Writing Fellowship. Recently, he was the Carol Houck Smith Fiction Fellow at the University of Wisconsin. His fiction has appeared in the *Atlantic*: his novel *The Book of Life* is published by Picador.

Sean O'Brien has written seven collections of poetry. *The Drowned Book* (2007) won the Forward and T. S. Eliot prizes. *Cousin Coat: Selected Poems 1976–2001* appeared in 2002. His other work includes the book of essays *The Deregulated Muse* (1998), the verse plays *The Birds* (2002) and *Keepers of the Flame* (2003), and a verse translation of Dante's *Inferno* (2006). In 2008 his collection of short stories, *The Silence Room*, was published, followed in 2009 by his novel *Afterlife*. Picador publish his *Collected Poems* in 2012. He is Professor of Creative Writing at Newcastle University.

Matteo Pericoli was born in Milan. He is best known for his illustrated books of New York, where he lived from 1995 to 2008, and for *London Unfurled*, his brilliant and utterly unprecedented portrait of London, published by Picador. His work is regularly featured in the *Observer*, the *New York Times* and *La Stampa*, Italy's national newspaper. He is currently living in Turin.

Anna Raverat was born in Cambridge and grew up in North Yorkshire with her parents, Lucy Raverat, a painter, and Andrew Rawlinson, an academic and writer, and her three younger siblings. She is descended from Gwendolin Raverat, a celebrated artist and member of the Bloomsbury group. Anna read English at King's College, Cambridge and now works as a consultant in organization development and leadership. She lives in London with her three children. *Signs of Life*, her first novel, is published by Picador.

Sarah Rayner grew up in London and now lives in Brighton. She is the bestselling author of *One Moment, One Morning*, which has been translated into eleven languages, and *The Two Week Wait*, both published by Picador. She worked for twenty years as an advertising copywriter, and now writes fiction full time.

Graham Robb was born in Manchester in 1958 and is a former Fellow of Exeter College, Oxford. He has published widely on French literature and history, including biographies of Victor Hugo (which won the Royal Society of Literature Heinemann Award and the Whitbread Biography Award in 1997) and Rimbaud (shortlisted for the Samuel Johnson Prize in 2000).

The Contributors

Picador publish *The Discovery of France*, which won both the Duff Cooper and Royal Society of Literature Ondaatje Prizes, and *Parisians: An Adventure History of Paris*, which was a *Sunday Times* Top Ten Bestseller. He is a Chevalier dans l'Ordre des Arts et des Lettres and a Fellow of the Royal Society of Literature, and lives on the English-Scottish border.

Robin Robertson is from the north-east coast of Scotland. His first collection, *A Painted Field*, won a number of prizes, including the 1997 Forward Prize for Best First Collection and the Saltire Scottish First Book of the Year Award. His second collection, *Slow Air*, was published in 2002. He received the 2004 E. M. Forster Award from the American Academy of Arts and Letters, and was selected by the Poetry Book Society as one of twenty Next Generation poets. *Swithering* was shortlisted for the 2006 T. S. Eliot Prize and won the Forward Prize. In 2009 he won the Forward Prize for his poem 'At Roane Head', which is included in his most recent collection, *The Wrecking Light* (2010), shortlisted for the T. S. Eliot Prize, the Costa Poetry Award and the Forward Prize. All these are available in Picador, and we publish his new collection, *Hill of Doors*, in 2013.

Jon Ronson is an award-winning writer and documentary maker. He is the author of three bestsellers, *Them: Adventures with Extremists*, *The Men Who Stare At Goats*, and *The Psychopath Test*, and two collections, *Out of the Ordinary: True Tales of Everyday Craziness* and *What I Do: More True Tales of Everyday Craziness*, all published by Picador, as is his new book, *Lost at Sea*, a collection of mini-adventure stories. He lives in London and New York.

Alice Sebold is the author of the bestselling novels *The Lovely Bones* and *The Almost Moon*, and the memoir *Lucky*, all published by Picador. She lives in California with her husband, the writer Glen David Gold.

Emma Straub lives in New York City. She is the author of a short-story collection, *Other People We Married*. Her first novel, *Laura Lamont's Life in Pictures*, is published by Picador.

Graham Swift was born in 1949 and is the author of nine acclaimed novels and a collection of short stories, all published by Picador. With *Waterland* he won the *Guardian* Fiction Prize (1983), and with *Last Orders* the Booker Prize (1996); both novels have since been made into films. His most recent novel is *Wish You Were Here*, *Time Out* Novel of the Year. Graham Swift's work has appeared in over thirty languages.

Miguel Syjuco was born and raised in Manila. A freelance writer, he has written for international publications, including the *New York Times*, the *International Herald Tribune*, the *Globe & Mail*, and the *CBC*. Picador published his novel *Ilustrado*, winner of the Man Asian Literary Prize, in 2011. He currently lives in Montreal.

Rebecca Wait has been writing for as long as she can remember and has won numerous prizes for short stories and plays. She

The Contributors

wrote her novel *The View on the Way Down*, to be published by Picador in 2013, in the evenings whilst working as a teaching assistant. Rebecca now lives in London.

Kevin Wilson is the author of the collection *Tunneling to the Center of the Earth*, which received the 2009 Shirley Jackson Award, and *The Family Fang*, published by Picador. He lives in Sewanee, Tennessee, with his wife, the poet Leigh Anne Couch, and his son, Griff, where he teaches fiction at the University of the South and helps run the Sewanee Writers' Conference.

Simon Winder was born in London in 1963, somewhat prematurely thanks to his mother's response to all the action and adventure in *From Russia with Love*. He is the editor of a number of anthologies, including the highly praised *Night Thoughts*. He works in publishing, most recently at Penguin where he had the perhaps slightly disturbing fan's apotheosis of actually buying the rights to Ian Fleming's novels. Picador publish *The Man Who Saved Britain* and *Germania*, his very personal guide to the Germany that he loves. He lives in Wandsworth Town.

Naomi Wood was born in 1983 and lives in London. She studied at Cambridge and at UEA for her MA in Creative Writing. Originally from York, she has gone on to live in Hong Kong, Paris and Washington DC. *The Godless Boys*, her first novel, is published by Picador.

The Contributors

Gerard Woodward is the author of an acclaimed trilogy comprising *August* (shortlisted for the 2001 Whitbread First Novel Award), *I'll Go to Bed at Noon* (shortlisted for the 2004 Man Booker Prize), and *A Curious Earth*. He was born in London in 1961, and published several prize-winning collections of poetry before turning to fiction. His collection of poetry *We Were Pedestrians* was shortlisted for the 2005 T. S. Eliot Prize, and Picador publish his new collection, *The Seacunny*. He is Professor of Creative Writing at Bath Spa University and his latest novel is *Nourishment*, also published by Picador.